REAL
FOOD
RECOVERY

The Busy Mom's Guide to Health & Healing - **with 92** Gluten Free, Casein Free (GFCF) Recipes

BY: MANDY BLUME, B.SC., NTP

Publishing services provided by:

 Archangel Ink

Printed in South Korea

Images provided by: Mandy Blume, Canva and Shutterstock

ISBN: 978-1-942761-81-5

For Jayce, Luke, Ian, Dak (in memoriam), and Jamie

This book is dedicated to all the beautiful children who lit the fire within me to be a better mom and spread the love!

Disclaimer:

Please note that the information in this book is offered as a reference for your own wellness strategy. I am sharing my experiences and discoveries for the purpose of opening your mind to what is possible. And most importantly, I recommend finding a holistic doctor and teaming up for a great ride. However, for legal purposes, we must state that any recommendations made and/or studies referred to in this book are not a substitute for consultation with a health-care provider.

What the Experts Are Saying

As a registered nurse in wound care, I have witnessed the power of love, good food, and natural products, which heal more than just the skin of a person. And I have found it important to blend natural health care with allopathic approaches when emergencies arise. Mandy Blume has a heart to empower people to eat better and heal through very simple recipes with a purpose. The research of best foods and efforts with foster children have brought forth this empowering cookbook that will help us all.

—Shannon Mastronardo, RN, WCC, and proud mom to four sons who own Nardo's Natural Organic Skincare and acquired an investment deal on TV's Shark Tank

Grains and dairy foods are important components of nourishing traditional diets; however, grains and milk products are the most difficult foods to digest and often need to be removed from the diet for healing to take place. Mandy Blume guides you through the process of going gluten-free and casein-free and provides delicious GFCF recipes, so that you never feel deprived.

—Sally Fallon Morell, president

The Weston A. Price Foundation

Finally, a cookbook oriented toward parents of kids with autism, ADHD, allergies, and other chronic conditions who need real help in the kitchen today. Nourishing our children with real food is a fundamental part of the healing process, but many parents don't know where to begin. Mandy Blume makes getting into the kitchen fun, easy, and enjoyable. This cookbook should be prescribed by every pediatrician who makes a chronic illness diagnosis.

—Beth Lambert, author of A Compromised Generation, executive director of Epidemic Answers and the Documenting Hope Project

It is rare to find a cookbook filled with recipes that are healthy, delicious, and practical. Yet Mandy Blume has done that with her book Real Food Recovery. She has shared countless tried-and-true dishes that she's used to nourish her family, as well as her many foster children. And in the process, these recipes have transformed their health. If you're looking for a hands-on cookbook that will get your family healthy and keep them that way, this is it! I highly recommend it.

—Maya Shetreat-Klein, MD, author of The Dirt Cure and founder of the Terrain Institute

Over half of our nation's children are chronically ill, learning disabled, and neurodevelopmentally impaired. Caloric intake notwithstanding, many kids are severely under- or overweight. As parents, we must be fearless to heal our children. It will almost surely mean going against conventional wisdom, social norms, medical advice, mainstream media, and the very best intentions of educators, colleagues, neighbors, family, and friends. This doesn't mean, however, that you're alone. Not when you can invite Mandy Blume into your kitchen. Want to know how to heal your child? Save time, tears, and money—buy this wonderful book.

—Louise Kuo Habakus, author, activist, Founder of FearlessParent.org

This book is about how we eat and help other children get better. It will help many people. There are so many important things that people do not even think of or really practice.

When my brother died, it changed our family and our lives. I hope that this book will make a positive change in the world. I hope it changes the way you eat and many other things.

My mommy loves us and many children, and we have helped many mean and sick children get better and become nice because they didn't know how. I hope no one else has to lose their brother.

—Ian, Mandy's son, seventh grader and intelligent, recovered brother and philanthropist for children and a Certified Traditional Food Cook through Simply Being Well

As a former licensing agent in the foster system for many years, I am so excited to recommend this cookbook! The agency watched as Mandy fought, in an unprecedented case, for her foster son against cancer. We knew that during his chemotherapy, Mandy would nourish his little soul and stomach with the best options. His strength between rounds of chemo was amazing.

The improved behavior changes of all the children placed into this loving family were noticeable. So if Mandy can help recover these precious children with her recipes filled with love, anyone can find a better level of health with the tips she shares. I recommend this book for any parent and foster parent seeking a simple way to support good health with foods we use in the kitchen.

—Nanny Vazquez, former foster care licensing agent

Contents

Foreward

It takes an enormous amount of diligence and love to nurture a child to health in today's environment. Yet, Mandy Blume has done it! With research and determination, this mom has taken to heart the work of many researchers and holistic practitioners to recover children in a very real way—through the kitchen. Mandy has even used her research to work within the constraints of foster care, helping many children recover by providing them with a real-food diet!

Taking it a step further, this beautiful, empowering cookbook of real-food recipes delivers dishes that are truly achievable for the busiest parent. Food is the most important modality that every family can use to heal. This wonderful cookbook will help many families reach a new level of health.

As stated so aptly in *Real Food Recovery*, food has a functional purpose. The way food is grown and harvested is very important. Mandy gets it and has helped many children reach an optimal level of health.

We must be mindful of the foods we put into our bodies and especially cognizant of the impact food has on the generation of sick kids today. As we spread the message and choose our food more wisely, we can and will redirect this destructive path and begin revitalizing our children, our families, and our societies, returning to healthy lifestyles and wholesome nourishment.

—Stephanie Seneff, PhD
Senior research scientist, MIT Computer Science and Artificial Intelligence Laboratory

Acknowledgments

Many people have touched my family and inspire us with their belief, support, courage, and knowledge. First, my thanks goes out to Dr. Goolsby Chiropractic for showing us a natural way, Dr. Walsh Chiropractic for perseverance, and Lori and Dr. Joe Christiano, ND, with Body Redesigning; Nanny Vazquez, our gifted foster care licensing agent and friend; Kristin Canty of Woods Hill Table and the film documentary *Farmageddon*; Dr. Stephanie Seneff, a brilliant MIT researcher; Beth Lambert of Epidemic Answers; Valerie Good with Abundant Life; Dr. Gonzales (in memoriam) for kindness and his cancer expertise; Sally Fallon and Dr. Mary Enig, authors of *Nourishing Traditions*; Gray Graham, founder of Nutritional Therapy Association; Caroline Barringer, NTA, instructor with the blog *Freeway Foodies*; Monica Corrado, chef and founder of Simply Being Well; Susan Marsicano and Bruce Weaver of Kissimmee Greens Farm; Elaine Boland with Fields of Athenry; and Joel Salatin of PolyFace Farms.

These are true celebrities who have inspired many because they are pioneers in their professions, from alternative and traditional medicine to farmers, restaurant owners, film producers, and parents—they all live with a courageous love for people, animals, and the earth.

It is important to acknowledge you, the reader! Throughout this book, I will use "we," because you are in this with me. Although we as people may have some differences in the kitchen and life, this book incorporates and embraces our common goal, which is the best health we all deserve!

Special gratitude is reserved for Talie, my first editor, and the incredible publishing and editing team (Kristie and Nichole) at Archangel Ink, and Dr. Joe Christiano for unique content advice!

Many thanks to our community, neighbors, and friends, especially Eleni and her beautiful (yet food-particular) girls, who sampled recipes and showed us the recipes to drop and the ones to keep. You rock!

I also want to thank Jackie Z. and Janine for donating the dress on the cover of this book. I so appreciate it!

Finally, I owe a great debt of gratitude to my family, whose love, support, and sacrifices enable me to reach out to a world in need of *hope!*

Chapter 1: The Beginning

When your doctor tells you that you or someone you love has a chronic illness, there is a great possibility that he or she will recommend a gluten-free, casein-free (GFCF) diet. A GFCF diet eliminates gluten and casein, which are the proteins found in many grain and dairy products. As you begin the journey:

be equipped;

be calm;

believe; and

be positive.

Although this may seem impossible right now, remember that *knowledge is power*, so pull yourself up by your bootstraps and join me on an exciting adventure.

Whether this new diet is recommended for you, a child, or a loved one, this book is intended to inspire a new perspective on food and GFCF. Eating GFCF seems to be at the root of many recovery diets, and many can attest to its success. Additionally, there are more and more studies showing the health benefits of eliminating gluten.[1] However, this change needs to be simple, so that people can make it. And since many doctors will tell you to start a GFCF diet, this brawny cookbook is meant to guide you through.

It has been my family's experience that many people are able to recover significantly and overcome the gluten and casein intolerance. It is not a guarantee, but by eating carefully for a season, future consumption of properly prepared grains and dairy foods may be possible. We have found the healing to be in the real food, meaning the food that has not been processed or modified so much.

When a disease reveals itself in your life, remember that there *is* a way toward recovery. Don't feel isolated or guilty, because you aren't alone in your challenges. My hope for this book is to share a bit of my family's journey and make yours a little easier by keeping the recipes, photos, and message authentic.

We are now living in an era where too many of us are sick, and diseases that were prevalent among the mature are now affecting the younger generation in unprecedented ways. I offer my family's success, encouragement, clarity, and delicious recipes to jumpstart your revelations toward recovery.

---

1   A. Di Sabatino et al., "Small Amounts of Gluten in Subjects with Suspected Nonceliac Gluten Sensitivity: A Randomized, Double-Blind, Placebo-Controlled, Cross-Over Trial," *Clinical Gastroenterology and Hepatology* 13, no. 9 (September 2015): 1604–1612, doi:10.1016/j.cgh.

Mandy's Story

Being the mother of four and a foster mom to many is busy, joyful, and challenging! For me, motherhood came not as a sweet and soft beginning, but more "warrior style" when my first biological child was born with severe complications that threatened his survival. Thanks to quick transitions and an evolving medical team, we powered through two years of intense care and intervention.

As our family grew, we developed better eating habits by choosing whole, nutritious foods and eliminating gluten and dairy for some children. We found *Nourishing Traditions*, by Sally Fallon and Mary Enig, and it rocked our world. Each subsequent child was born progressively healthier, but we were heartbroken when our oldest began exhibiting behaviors characteristic of the autistic spectrum after vaccination.

Despite these challenges, we pursued the dream of welcoming orphans into our family by fostering local children in need with the hope of ultimately adopting them. When it seemed that every child we took in was sick with some chronic illness (our first foster son had cancer at age two), we realized that our biological children's circumstances were not unique. But thanks to good nutrition and lots of love, all of our kiddos have experienced a significant degree of recovery. That's an empowering experience that everyone can appreciate.

In the past six years, we've been privileged to love many wonderful foster kids. Needless to say, we take our food very seriously . . . and life, well, not so much! We make the most of our time together and have seen miracles with a real-food, GFCF diet. Today, I am committed to sharing our stories via Real Food Recovery (RealFoodRecovery.org), a website and nonprofit company that focuses on raising healthy families and helping foster kids. I also volunteer, cook, and teach other medical professionals and parents (biological and adoptive) wherever I can.

There are many ways to heal and reach some level of recovery for our kids. If I can help so many recover within my own home and within the constraints of a foster system, I have no doubt that anyone can be empowered to do the same. Welcome to my kitchen. Be passionate about life and wellness!

A New Approach

It's inspiring how we can do anything for our children: waking in the night to check a new baby's breathing, putting on a brave face for their first day of class, lifting a two-ton truck off a child pinned underneath, you name it. From the start, we are tuned-in to their patterns and preferences, and it continues as we watch them grow. It makes no difference if the child is birthed, fostered, or adopted—each child grabs your heart. We moms come to know things, and we can tell if something is not right with our children. It can be difficult to face our children's illnesses, but sometimes the solutions are simpler than we've been taught by society.

Despite an almost virulent epidemic of childhood illnesses, allergies, and developmental disorders, our cultural practice is to shove food into hungry bodies without considering whether it's beneficial. Then we race to the next new doctor, hoping to be healed. Recovery can happen this way, but it can happen better with good, real food.

Quite simply, I have come to understand that each bite we take either helps us, neither helps nor hurts us, or hurts us. Food is the fuel that runs our bodies. And when our health is compromised, we must change the fuel and make it cleaner.

Here are the basic tenets of my approach to cleaner eating:

No one diet will work for every single person. Our bodies have their own intelligence, and we must tune in to the signals they send.

Everything in moderation. Even if something is nutritious, don't eat it every day forever. Utilize variety so boredom doesn't creep in. Life is about balance. Too much of anything can be harmful.

Balance between raw and cooked food. My system is to eat 50 percent raw and 50 percent cooked (and not cooked to ashes). Again, balance is important.

Casein and gluten have wreaked havoc on enough people that I feel confident eliminating them is a surefire way to jumpstart the recovery process. And again, this restriction isn't necessarily forever. Those in our family who have recovered enjoy raw goat's milk and yogurt from our farm friends.

The next step is to consider the indication you're dealing with, whether it's IBS, celiac disease, autism, cancer, mitochondrial disorder, ADD, diabetes, eczema, or some other condition, then reduce foods known to exacerbate that condition. Be patient if you forget to omit foods that might cause harm. It's impossible to be perfect. However, following a healthier lifestyle does get easier with time.

Sugar and the Moment of Change

The greatest offense made in the GFCF-elimination process is adding processed, sugary foods into a GFCF diet. I have seen children and adults hindered in recovery due to this highly processed "GFCF" replacement. It blows my mind that we have such an affection for sugar.

Did you know that one tablespoon of commercial applesauce is higher in sugar than a tablespoon of granulated sugar? Food manufacturers keep ramping up the sweet factor in everything from juice to ketchup to fruit cups, because society tends to buy it. It tastes (and feels) good. But we have to be smarter.

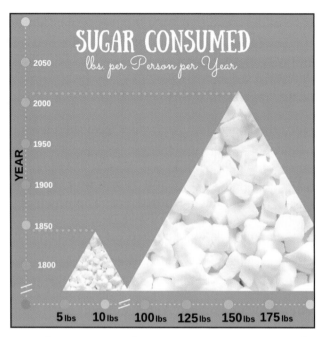

Over the past 150 years, we have increased sugar consumption nearly twenty times more per person per year. Sugar is put into most processed foods we buy, even the so-called healthy pre-packaged products. There was a short time when I bought every processed, packaged cookie, pizza, and flour out there that touted itself as gluten-free. Then I realized the importance of real food and reduced the processed food that is really stripped of nutrients and full of sugar, starch, and corn. Keeping GFCF with more real food was the magic combination for positive change!

I am not a doctor . . . yet. But as a mom in college again, becoming a certified nutritional therapy practitioner a few years ago was a great first step to health. After earning a bachelor of science degree and pursuing pre-med coursework, I built a real-food foundation on health through this certification. My success is collaboration through education, thinking outside of the box, and finding great partners for health-care practitioners. Taking ownership within my sphere of control, grabbing the reins of nutrition, and feeding my family well feels great. Not so long ago, I had that "deer in the headlights" moment: that moment when it's clear a child needs help, and you realize that the applesauce you've been giving your child isn't so healthy after all. The heart drops, the mind reels, but then that mommy instinct kicks in and says, "There has to be something I can do, and I'm going to find it!"

On that note, not everyone agrees exactly which diet is the key to optimal health—Paleo? GAPS? Vegetarian? Mediterranean? Weston A. Price? Primal? Atkins?—and that is OK. The goal is to expand your concept of good-for-you foods and help you integrate any of these diets into your repertoire. In fact, let's incorporate all of these diets as far as they are real-food and GFCF. My family's delicious recipes are simple and have helped many develop an appetite for healthier foods. But best of all, they've been a vital part of restoring wellness. Most are easy, others get easier with practice, and all of them are quite quick to prepare! My hope is that this collection will be your go-to resource for inspiration when headed to the kitchen.

Here's to you, your instinct, and your moment of change! It's an honor to support you on your journey.

Chapter 2: What? GFCF Recipes?

"What were you thinking?" you ask. When the doctor told my family that dropping gluten and casein from our diet would optimize the health of my children, I thought, "What?" Then, of course, I was ready. "No wheat. No milk. I can handle that. Game on!"

But my first trip to the grocery store was a real eye-opener. It seemed that gluten and casein were in practically every packaged food I'd grown accustomed to buying. Suddenly, all of my family's food options were shut down, or so I thought.

Sound familiar?

Don't despair!

A Little History on Processed Food

So much has changed in the last century. Entities known as "food giants" began in the early 1900s after the Industrial Revolution, and they flourished with the onset of World War II. They steered communities away from small-scale, seasonal suppliers and toward food that was processed, packaged, or monocropped. Later, food was increasingly modified, or "stabilized," during World War II to increase its shelf life, so that it could be sent overseas. Bread, for example, was estimated to have lost some twenty-plus nutrients in the process, most of which are still missing in today's store-bought varieties.[2]

Deficiency of these very nutrients has been implicated in a host of health problems plaguing kids today—but hey!—bread doesn't bruise or go moldy, so it's worth it. Not. Today, societies across the globe are demonstrating the inability of our bodies to digest gluten; thus, the growing awareness of the benefits of a gluten-free diet.

And that's the key difference. Modern grandparents often respond to today's food allergies and restricted diets with a comment like, "We never worried about any of those things. We ate whatever we wanted, and look at us. We're fine!" What they're forgetting is that it's not just a matter of the food in question, but everything *about* it: where it's purchased, who grew it and where, how it was modified before we even see it on the shelf. In the average American supermarket, these are virtually unanswerable questions. This food-giant model persists almost one hundred years later.

---

2   Henry A. Schroeder, "Losses of Vitamins and Trace Minerals Resulting from Processing and Preservation of Foods," *American Journal of Clinical Nutrition* 24, no. 5 (1971): 562–573.

Time to Get Real

Are you convinced to reduce processed foods yet? Picking up this book is a step in the right direction! And take heart: reducing prepackaged snacks and convenience food is not as hard as you might first think at first. Remember, GFCF should be *real, whole foods* that will improve health but, most importantly, taste delicious! And without the drain of allergic response, the body has more energy to function and recover.

Of course, the needs of compromised children take priority in a family's schedule. Realistically, it is not feasible to spend all day in the kitchen "gourmeting" and still manage the daily load. With that in mind, let's focus on efficiency in the kitchen. So, are you ready? Let's rock it!

Chapter 3: Awareness

GFCF didn't seem like such a big deal at first; it is just eliminating milk and bread from our diet. Boy, that was wrong. The list of unacceptable foods and ingredients is long—way too long to remember. So, this "awareness page" is a cheat sheet that was four years in the making. Note that some of these items can be found or made GFCF, such as vitamins or spices. If it is marked "check," research that particular item on a case-by-case basis.

And always, always, always read the ingredients! Just remember that companies often change ingredients and your best bet is food from the dirt, a tree, or a pastured animal with space to move.

Foods with Gluten to Avoid or Check

» Baking powder – check

» Baking soda – check

» Barley grain and flour

» Barley malt

» Beer

» Bleached all-purpose flour

» Bouillon cubes and powder

» Bran

» Bread flour

» Broth (prepackaged)

» Bulgur

» Caramel coloring

» Cereal

» Coffee creamer substitutes

» Couscous

» Croutons

» Durum grain and flour

» Einkorn wheat

» Enriched flour

» Farina

» Fu (dried wheat gluten)

» Glutamate (any derivative)

» Gluten flour

» Graham flour

» Gravy cubes and mixes

» Ground spices – check

» Gum base

» Hard wheat

» Herbs with wheat fillers

» Kamut

» Malt extract, flavoring, syrup, vinegar

» Miso

» Modified food starch (sourced from corn or wheat)

» MSG (made outside the United States)

» Mustard powder – check

» Oat flour

» Oats – check

» Pasta

» Pearl barley

» Rice syrup

» Semolina derivatives and flour

» Shoyu (soy sauce)

» Spelt

» Teriyaki sauce

» Vitamins – check

» Wheat Germ

Foods with Casein to Avoid

- » Artificial butter flavor
- » Butter*
- » Butter fat
- » Buttermilk
- » Butter oil
- » Casein (hydrosylate)
- » Caseinates
- » Cheese
- » Condensed milk
- » Cottage cheese
- » Cream*
- » Crème fraîche*
- » Curds
- » Custard
- » Dry milk
- » Evaporated milk
- » Ghee*
- » Goat's milk*
- » Half-and-half
- » Hot dogs
- » Lactose (any derivative)
- » Lunchmeat
- » Malt
- » Margarine
- » Milk (all forms and preparations)
- » Nondairy creamer
- » Nougat
- » Powdered milk
- » Pudding

- » Rennet casein
- » Sausage
- » Sour cream*
- » Yogurt*

The items marked with an asterisk indicate what may be considered controversial ingredients, because they either contain significantly lower amounts of casein or, in some cases, can disputably be obtained without casein. Their nutritional benefit makes the investigation worth the effort. For example, studies show that a very bio-available protein is found in yogurt that provides vitamin D and strengthens the immune system.[3] (Likely, it's the cultured part that really helps nutritionally, so a recipe for some delicious GFCF-friendly yogurt follows this section.)

It is also a worthy note that milk has a historical reputation for healing. An article written by Dr. J. R. Crewe of the Mayo Foundation—forerunner of the Mayo Clinic in Rochester, Minnesota—published in *Certified Milk Magazine* stated many benefits to milk. Today, however, milk delivery has changed. Formerly, milk was raw and from a local farmer. Today, it's mass-produced, cooked, and put in a container at a local grocery chain.

Additionally, depending on where you research, it is debatable if clarified ghee contains casein. Some studies contend that the casein is removed in the clarifying process and other studies state there are trace amounts remaining. Many children are able to take a specific brand, Pure Indian Foods Cultured Ghee, because the casein is so very low. Therefore, it is included as an option in our recipes, but you have to evaluate what works best for you. Finally, there are certain goat breeds (Alpine and Saarinen) that have no [A1] casein whatsoever in their milk.[4]

---

3   E. M. Selhub, A. C. Logan, and A. C. Bested, "Fermented Foods, Microbiota, and Mental Health: Ancient Practice Meets Nutritional Psychiatry," *Journal of Physiological Anthropology* 33, no. 2 (January 15, 2014), doi:10.1186/1880-6805-33-2.

4   Whyara Karoline Almeida de Costa et al., "Comparative Protein Composition Analysis of Goat Milk Produced by the Alpine and Saanen Breeds in Northeastern Brazil and Related Antibacterial Activities," *PLoS One* 9, no. 3 (March 27, 2014), doi:10.1371/journal.pone.0093361.

Homemade GFCF Yogurt

This homemade yogurt is a delicious, age-old remedy with GFCF modifications. Yogurt is full of good flora that will help repopulate the gut, but go slowly. It is important to take a small portion to allow your gut to be slowly introduced to these probiotics. Filling a bowl to the brim with delicious yogurt may cause some unnecessary side effects (frequent trips to the loo). Starting with small portions is wise (¼ cup was a good start for us). Pick one (or both) of the options below and see which one you like best.

Option 1:

- 5 (15-ounce) cans coconut milk, warmed to around 170°F
- ¼ cup raw honey
- 4 tablespoons plain grass-fed beef gelatin
- ½ teaspoon GFCF probiotic (2- to 3-strain yogurt starter)

Place the coconut milk in a large bowl. Add the raw honey and gelatin, stirring well to combine. Let the mixture cool until it is 75°F to 80°F. Add the probiotic. Stir again and divide the mixture evenly between 2 (1-quart) glass jars.

Put the lids on the jars and place them in the oven. Turn on the oven light, but do not turn the oven on. Let the yogurt sit in the oven overnight or up to 24 hours.

Remove the cultured yogurt from the oven and refrigerate. Generally, we eat the yogurt within a week. (We have stored it up to a month in the refrigerator, but it gets really strong.)

Option 2:

- 2 cups fresh coconut meat
- ½ cup filtered water
- ¼ teaspoon GFCF probiotic (2- to 3-strain yogurt starter)

Blend the coconut meat and filtered water in a blender until it is smooth. Transfer the coconut mixture to a large bowl and stir in the probiotic. Divide the mixture evenly between 2 (1-quart) glass jars.

Put the lids on the jars and place them in the oven. Turn on the oven light, but do not turn the oven on. Let the yogurt sit in the oven overnight or up to 24 hours.

Remove the cultured yogurt from the oven and refrigerate. This fresh version tends to have a shorter shelf life (around 2 weeks).

Today, there are some pretty amazing holistic MDs and PhDs who are discussing, researching, and recommending a simplified diet and noting improvements. Their research studies how your body should function and the foods that seem to help compromised health. Studies I have found helpful discuss processes like eNOS, restarting macrophage, and the benefits of vitamin D, nitric oxide, and yogurt.[5] Therefore, these elements (which are easily obtainable) are incorporated into the recipes. Try them—they may provide some recovery through your kitchen.

---

5   Stephanie Seneff, Robert M. Davidson, and Jingjing Liu, "Empirical Data Confirm Autism Symptoms Related to Aluminum and Acetaminophen Exposure," *Entropy* 14 (2012): 2227–2253, doi:10.3390/e14112227; Simin Nikbin Meydani and Woel-Kyu Ha, "Immunologic Effects of Yogurt," *American Journal of Clinical Nutrition* 71, no. 4 (April 2000): 861–872; Lynda Thyer et al., "GC Protein-Derived Macrophage-Activating Factor Decreases α-N-Acetylgalactosaminidase Levels in Advanced Cancer Patients," *OncoImmunology* 2, no. 8 (2013), doi:10.4161/onci.25769; Lynda Thyer, Jacopo J.V. Branca, Margit Taubmann, "Clinical Experience of Immunotherapy Based on Oleic Acid Bound to Glycosylated Vitamin D-Binding Protein in Localised and Metastatic Adenocarcinoma of the Pancreas," *Anticancer Research* 34, no. 10 (2014): 5847–5849.

Chapter 4: Paradigm (and Pyramid) Shift

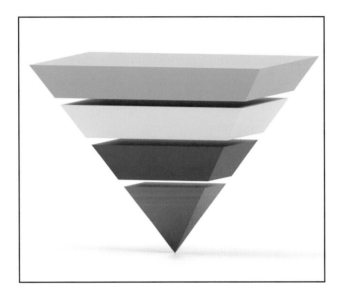

Many would just write off hope and expect you to accept the new diagnosis you are facing, whether it's attention disorder, celiac disease, IBS, mitochondrial disorder, birth defect, or autism, as if some verdict has been given.

Just say, "No!"

Believe

If disorder in the body can happen, surely it can "unhappen," at least to some degree. In chemistry, it's called "equilibrium," in medicine it's called "homeostasis." Consider three particular things about the recovery process:

We are not defined by a disease. Rather, we are defined by how we react, persevere, live, and, hopefully, overcome a disease. And with diligence, we can move toward a wonderful level of recovery.

Education is paramount. This was certainly not a chosen path for any of us, but the resulting self-awareness and empowerment is great. The good news is that your entire family will begin to feel and look better! The bad news is that it genuinely sucks at first. But somehow, the real food actually begins to taste good in about two weeks.

Convenience must be reinvented. Compromised health adds another level complication to the race of life. But fast food is no longer an acceptable plan B dinner. Fortunately, I've got lots of alternatives for you! It will just require a shift in thinking. Four shifts, in fact.

At this point, you may be thinking, "Haven't I already had enough sudden change dumped on me?" Yes, but this will help you live well through it.

It is overwhelming. But trust me—these four shifts will be worth the discomfort of transition. You just have to cross over your fear to land in a new place of wonderfulness.

Shift 1: Work Toward a Real, Whole-Food, GFCF Diet

Remember the food pyramid, the one with all the bread, gluten, and processed foods (including cereal) forming a base at the bottom? That pyramid represents what is known as the standard American diet, which is truly useless for recovering health. The whole thing is upside down. Therefore, let's simply flip the whole thing on its head, and our health will be much more likely to improve.

Our bodies actually need more good saturated fats, like coconut oil, tallow, poultry fat, and red palm oil. To paraphrase Dr. Mary Enig, fat surrounds all of our vital organs and is truly a brain food.[6] Fortunately, I have lots of recipes and techniques for integrating these nutrient-dense fats into your GFCF diet.

And while we're on the subject of fat, let's just establish right now that margarine is *not* a real food. It is liquid oil at room temperature that is first hydrogenated then infused with nickel to become and remain a solid fat at room temperature. Then it is bleached to remove its gray color, while yellow food coloring is added to look like butter. Could it be any stranger? Although it is casein-free, there is no value to this "Franken-butter."[7] I cited a study here, but mere common sense reveals this is not food for us or our children. Please don't put it on your roster of acceptable GFCF fats!

Instead, use good fats noted above. These fats are simply pressed (squeezed) out of the fruit or it is separated from the meat and clarified through heating at a low temperature with water. This is a whole food that nourishes children and adults.

---

6   Mary Enig, *Know Your Fats: The Complete Primer for Understanding the Nutrition of Fats, Oils, and Cholesterol* (Silver Spring, MD: Bethesda Press, 2000).

7   Mary Enig and Sally Fallon, "The Oiling of America," pts. 1 and 2, *NEXUS* magazine 6, no. 1 (December 1998–January 1999); 6, no. 2 (February–March 1999).

Shift 2: Enjoy Healthy Foods

It's a new perspective and there is a learning curve. Whether you are learning a new workout routine, riding a bike, learning to play an instrument, or changing to a Real Food Recovery diet, it's not easy at first. Then all of a sudden, you realize that you're getting into it, even enjoying yourself. Give yourself time.

Your new "fast food" is the grocery store produce section or the farmer's market, where delicious and real gluten-free, casein-free food options are available.

Shift 3: Recognize That Foods Can Strengthen or Deplete Us

Processed-food manufacturers would distract and entertain us with dinosaur shapes and crinkle cuts, but we all know that the purpose of food is nourishment, so be strong, stay calm, and resist! Of course, no one is perfect, and sometimes there are moments of weakness, but by simply being aware and endeavoring to make better choices, we're already much better off than we were before.

Also, it is important to understand bio-individual needs. Every person is different, which is why blood tests and saliva tests are so helpful (as well as simply paying attention to how you feel after eating). If beef induces fatigue, eat chicken. If red meat and poultry are not working, try wild-caught fish. It's important to find the magic balance. A friend, Dr. Joe Christiano, introduced me to the practice of evaluating our blood types and eating the optimal foods. Although not followed 100 percent in our family, this method really helps with our energy levels and many children recover faster.

Shift 4: Preparation of Food is Optimal, but Don't Feel Guilty

Eating a real, whole-food, GFCF diet can be fun. And the guideline of eating homemade food as often as possible is certainly not always followed. So here is a caveat: do as much as you can.

Life must be enjoyed. We learn and get educated and then do as we can. If we feel guilty all the time for what we can't do, then that can be harmful. So don't go there.

Another help in preparation is with the food itself. The best way to make our food more digestible is to be grateful for what we have and then prepare the food a bit before eating. Soaking grains, nuts, and beans is something our grandparents did, but we are learning again. In fact, we are not what we eat, but what we can digest of what we eat. When a body is sick, the less work required to digest the food means the better our body absorbs nutrients. Soaking does just that. It pulls out phytates, which are anti-nutrients, because without soaking these phytates actually pull minerals out of your system during digestion. However, preparing makes a huge difference and takes a little planning in the kitchen. Not much, but a little. It's worth it when you can do it.

Be encouraged and enthusiastic for whatever you can manage. It will be an improvement.

Chapter 5: United We Stand

It's true that life pulls us all in a million directions. But we all need to eat. And though one's son might have autism, and another's daughter allergies, we are all fighting for good health. Our shared goal is for a better life and the highest possible level of recovery.

Our Common Ground

Here's a staggering statistic: one-third of the population of the United States is dealing with chronic illness.[8] That means we are part of a community about 117 million strong. Doesn't seem so rare when we are united!

---

8   Centers for Disease Control and Prevention, *Preventing Chronic Disease: Eliminating the Leading Preventable Causes of Premature Death and Disability in the United States* (Atlanta, GA: Centers for Disease Control and Prevention, n.d.).

Refuse to be hopeless. We must survive and thrive, for ourselves and for our kids. Because there *is* always hope. Already, by becoming more conscious consumers, we have changed the way food is served and grown. We are making a difference. Look at the packaging of food today. We have demanded and won labels that indicate gluten-free, non-GMO, organic, kosher, vegan, and more. Each label represents something to help us in our efforts to heal.

Instead of debating which is the most important label, let us join forces. Regardless of the diet you are on, let's figure out how to keep our food real and unite in our efforts to heal.

Let's focus on our common ground, which is to eat safe, beneficial food, prepared in a way to that will allow us to absorb the most nutrients. We all want to be independent and live to the fullest. (And to have some fun!)

This is where the spirit of this book will remain: on the common ground of our collective possibility.

Anything Is Possible with Hope

When the medical diagnosis offered a bleak prognosis, you *knew* there was something more. Something inside you screamed, "Beat the odds and recover." Listen to that voice—it is the voice of hope and determination.

Though we always hope for full recovery, know without a doubt it is important to delight in any level of recovery! "Winning" takes on a whole new meaning when you finally connect through a few words or make eye contact with an autistic child, an eleven-year-old stays dry through the night, a fifteen-year-old ADHD youth is equipped to read, or you hear, "The cancer is gone."

Keep pushing to win. Revel in each success, because every little improvement is worthy of celebration. And anything can happen if you have hope—so let's open the doors of our kitchens with a whole new possibility!

Chapter 6: The Doorway of Possibility . . . into the Kitchen

Food is comfort. Food is emotional. And the kitchen is where friends and families meet and conversations abound. It is also the portal to our health and our recovery. It is vital that this space be filled with love, so the food can be an extension of that love. If there is stress and resentment, the food will also exude this. So keep it peaceful and beautiful . . . and enjoy!

Another New Diet?

Back in 2010, the Centers for Disease Control and Prevention reported that seven of ten deaths in America were caused by chronic illness, indicating a decline in public health that has likely since continued its downward trajectory.[9]

Of course, many aspects of society contribute to its overall wellness. But the fact that our cultural diet and food sources have become so industrialized begs the question of their safety. Genetic modification, artificial ripening, global transportation, pesticides, herbicides, and chemical additives: we are talking, after all, about what we put into these bodies of ours.

To make matters worse, studies show that more than one-third of the population in America eats less than one fruit or vegetable per day.[10] This makes one wonder: How are we even getting vitamins and minerals? Do we just take pills for everything? No wonder everyone's searching for an answer.

Unfortunately, there are so many diets today that it gets a bit confusing. What, in fact, is the best way to eat for optimum health?

In *Real Food Recovery*, I recommend a whole-foods change and not one particular regimen; rather, you can take the principles and apply them to your own preferred way of eating. Since many doctors recommend a GFCF diet to heal and patients have seen the value, it is vital to demystify GFCF and inspire more real-food cooking.

And there are options when you have allergies. For example, if you find that you are allergic to chicken eggs, try your local farmer's market for duck, goose, or quail eggs. Another egg might work. The allergens we face force us to be creative, so keep trying.

The key, friends, is delicious real-food ingredients that are in season. It's time to put the pieces back together and get back into the kitchen!

The Right Tools

Here is a short but expensive list of awesome kitchen tools that make life a lot easier and reduce time in the kitchen. These tools range from $12 to $400, and it took me some time to acquire them.

Take the time you need. And be creative. Just know that getting back into the kitchen is not so bad when you acquire the right tools that make it fun and very convenient!

---

9   "FastStats: Deaths and Mortality," Centers for Disease Control and Prevention, last modified September 30, 2015, www.cdc.gov/nchs/fastats/deaths.htm.

10   "Chronic Diseases: The Leading Causes of Death and Disability in the United States," Centers for Disease Control and Prevention, last modified January 20, 2016, www.cdc.gov/chronicdisease/overview/index.htm.

If you don't have these items or can't afford them, there are options. Secondhand shops have many of these items for a great value:

- » High-speed blender
- » Water filter
- » Ice cream maker
- » Slow cooker
- » Immersion blender
- » Strainer
- » Mason jars (quart size)
- » Food processor

Chapter 7: A Tall Drink of Water

Yes, a nice glass of wine certainly comes to mind when dealing with the difficulties of ill health. But the very first step on the path to good nutrition is to drink enough water. Water is one of the most vital elements to our health.

Whenever possible, use a water filter. Put one on your faucet, buy a filtered pitcher, or install a filter in your plumbing. It will help remove contaminants such as chlorine, fluoride, metals, and harmful bacteria.

The goal is to drink around half of your body weight in ounces of water every day. For example, a 150-pound person is advised to drink around 75 ounces of good, clean water every day.

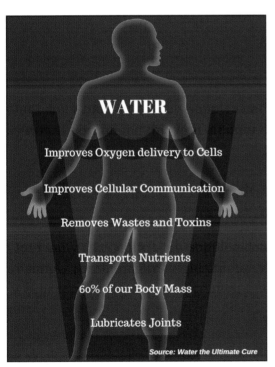

WATER

Improves Oxygen delivery to Cells

Improves Cellular Communication

Removes Wastes and Toxins

Transports Nutrients

60% of our Body Mass

Lubricates Joints

Source: Water the Ultimate Cure

So many adults and children won't drink water, or at least not enough, because it has no taste. But teas and juices are loaded with sugars and can be dehydrating. This is a major problem today, and too many bad calories are consumed in drinking without the benefit of hydration!

"Don't Treat Thirst with Medication"

So, what can we do to make hydrating taste better? Dr. F. Batmanghelidj writes in his book, *Your Body's Many Cries for Water*, how he healed many ailments with water alone. His concept is brilliant and forthrightly identifies the power of how simple and uncomplicated healing can be.

Our family takes quite a few supplements to treat various conditions, but if we could reduce them by simply consuming the right amount of water, I'd drink to that!

Get creative when it comes to hydrating. Putting pretty fruits and vegetables in the water is simple, adds taste, and helps us drink more water. To help you in your water journey, a few fun ideas to start the day are included on the following pages.

Lemony Morning Life Drink

The lemon gets your "ases" working: amylase, lipase, and others. These enzymes will help digest food so your body can utilize the nutrients you are eating. Don't underestimate the value of this simple addition to your day. And it gets your bum moving, too!

- 1 lemon wedge
- 1 to 2 cups hot or cold filtered water

Add the lemon to a glass of hot or cold filtered water. Enjoy!

On-the-Go Lemon Water

This quick drink is like lemonade with raw honey!

- 1 teaspoon bottled lemon juice
- 1 to 2 cups filtered water
- 1 teaspoon raw honey

Add the lemon juice to the filtered water. Add the raw honey for a touch of sweetness.

Natural Electrolyte Water

This is an additive- and preservative-free sports drink.

- 1 teaspoon Mineral-Enriched Water *(page 109)*
- 1 lemon or orange wedge
- 1 to 2 cups filtered water

Add the Mineral-Enriched Water and the lemon or orange wedge to the filtered water.

Apple Cider Vinegar Shots

This drink really cleanses your body. It is actually used to help cows produce babies! Apple cider vinegar has also been shown to reduce oxidative stress with high amounts of cholesterol.[11] No claims, but this is a great drink for many purposes.

- 1 shot (2 Ounces) apple cider vinegar
- 1 tablespoon raw honey
- 8 ounces warm or cold filtered water

Stir the apple cider vinegar and raw honey into the filtered water.

---

11   Y. Omura and S. L. Beckman, "Role of Mercury (Hg) in Resistant Infections and Effective Treatment of Chlamydia Trachomatis and Herpes Family Viral Infections (and Potential Treatment for Cancer) by Removing Localized Hg Deposits with Chinese Parsley and Delivering Effective Antibiotics Using Various Drug Uptake Enhancement Methods," *Acupuncture and Electro-Therapeutics Research* 20, nos. 3–4 (August–December 1995): 195–229.

Cool Cucumber Electrolyte Water

This recipe will cleanse and refresh you from the inside out!

- 3 cucumbers, sliced
- 1 bunch mint leaves
- 8 cups filtered water or sparkling mineral water

Place the cucumbers and mint leaves in a pitcher and muddle them. Add the filtered or sparkling water. Let this sit for 1 hour to infuse the flavor into the water.

Vitamin C Tea

Here's a drink to boost your immune system and your mood.

- 4 bags hibiscus tea
- 2 oranges, sliced
- 1 gallon filtered water

Add the tea bags and oranges to the filtered water and steep as a cold brew. (It takes just a few hours sitting out on the counter.)

Vitamin C Rush

Here's a rush for your immune system. Your body will thank you.

- 3 lemons, sliced
- 3 oranges, sliced
- 1 cup pineapple chunks (preferably fresh)
- 1 to 2 gallons filtered water

Place lemons, oranges, and pineapple into a large pitcher and muddle them. Add the filtered water. Let this sit for 1 hour to infuse the flavor into the water. This can last a couple of days, just add ice once a day.

Chapter 8: Bones Do a Body Good

Broths and stocks are extolled in the nutritional world for packing a nutrient-dense wallop. Not only are they super rich in minerals, they also help balance stomach acid, replace the mucosal lining of the gut[12], and even deworm. Potent stuff!

---

12 W. Y. Chen and G. Abatangelo, "Functions of Hyaluronan in Wound Repair," *Wound Repair and Regeneration* 7, no. 2 (March–April 1997): 79–89; U. Ravnskov et al., "Studies of Dietary Fat and Heart Disease," *Science* 295, no. 5559 (February 22, 2002): 1464–1466.

The Value of Broth and Stock

The difference between broth and stock is that broth is brewed longer with mostly bones and a little meat, whereas stock is simmered for less time with bones, meat, and organs (when they are available). Vegetable stock is just vegetables cooked in water for a long time. It contains vitamins and minerals, but no collagen.

The gelatinous collagen in both bone broth and stock has many benefits, such as the reduction of joint pain. Because of the higher meat ratio in stock, it seems to work better for dealing with a chronic illness. Stock is a gentler elixir for leaky and compromised guts. The uptake of proteins is utilized better through stocks, and protein is truly needed to absorb many vitamins and minerals. However, on occasion we've had a child whose flora was so out of balance that even meat stock caused an issue. No sweat! If this happens, just eliminate this food for a while. Use a milder vegetable stock instead until the gut is healed and sealed. You'll know because the child's behavior and temperament will improve.

You know how great restaurants will often keep house-made stock on hand to use as a base for many dishes? Well, we had a pleasant surprise when we brewed our own homemade version to heal the kids' guts. It totally elevated our home cooking to something like fine dining! Just swapping out stock for water in soups, mashed potatoes, and sauces made everything *so* much more delish. And believe it or not, a nice, warm cup of stock is also a yummy, nourishing way to start your day, unlike a bowl of cereal, which feeds the abnormal flora that we *don't* want in our gut.

Child after child has experienced tremendous improvements as a result of incorporating first stock then broth into their diets. This is a fundamental practice of Weston A. Price and the GAPS diet. GAPS is consumption of strictly broth and stock until your indications improve, and then you can add a new food. This can be a difficult but highly effective healing protocol that requires major commitment. It was designed by Natasha Campbell-McBride, MD, a brilliant neurologist and nutritionist who actually recovered her autistic son and became a much sought-after holistic practitioner in England. This is her personal story, but her professional notoriety is her successful practice and book, *Gut and Psychology Syndrome Diet*.[13]

However, by just incorporating the principles of Weston A. Price and my grandmother, you will experience recovery. Try incorporating stock into your diet; it will revolutionize your kitchen and your body!

---

13 www.gaps.me. This is Dr. Campbell-McBride's website, where you can read more about her and the GAPS diet.

Mom to Mom

It seems that we change diets almost as often as we change our clothes. When it comes to the latest health fad, a vulnerable, desperate parent or sick person will try anything.

Honestly, broth and stock are real game changers that have been used for thousands of years until about one hundred years ago. After our romance with processed foods began, we must have just forgotten about it! Yet there are some remaining elders in their 80s and 90s who are dying at a respectable old age, and they would tell you that one of their generation's dietary staples was soup.

My husband thought soup was boring and only came from a can. But when we changed our diet and began making stock and broth; the sumptuous, savory homemade version of soup became his favorite meal. He was amazed at how much better everything tasted.

Consuming homemade broth and stock is a good way to help us look and feel great. And I've seen the benefits with each foster child we've ever taken in. It only takes a little love and stock every day to see these sick kids improve noticeably. Behavior modulates, bowels regulate, and much more.

—Mandy

Fast and Furious I: Two Meals in One

Meal 1: Lovely Roasted Chicken or Beef

Yields 4 to 6 servings

This roasted chicken or chuck roast is perfect for a fall supper. Eat up!

- 1 to 2 (4- to 5-pound) whole chickens or 1 (4-pound) chuck roast with bones
- 4 carrots, cut into 1-inch pieces
- 2 stalks celery, cut into 1-inch pieces
- 1 (16-ounce) bag frozen broccoli or 1 pound fresh chopped green beans
- 2 onions, quartered
- 2 garlic cloves, crushed
- 3 to 5 potatoes
- ½ teaspoon salt
- ½ teaspoon turmeric
- ½ teaspoon paprika
- ½ teaspoon curry powder
- ½ teaspoon dried thyme
- ½ dried oregano
- 2 cups filtered water

Preheat the oven to 325°F. Rinse off the chicken or chuck roast in the sink.

Place the chicken or chuck roast, carrots, celery, broccoli or green beans, onions, garlic, and potatoes in a large roasting pan. Sprinkle the salt, turmeric, paprika, curry powder, thyme, and oregano over the meat and vegetables. Pour in the water.

Roast the meat and vegetables, uncovered, for 2 hours. Serve the meat and reserve the bones and remains for broth and stock.

Meal 2: A Delicious Soup

Yields 4 to 6 servings

There's nothing like getting extra mileage out of ingredients. This soup makes great use of the bones from the Lovely Roasted Chicken or Beef recipe.

- Bones and meaty bits from the Lovely Roasted Chicken or Beef recipe
- 1 onion, quartered
- 2 stalks celery, halved
- 2 carrots, halved
- ½ pound available organ meat (gizzards, necks, and feet for chicken; heart or liver for beef; optional, but healing)
- 1 to 2 tablespoons apple cider vinegar
- 1 gallon filtered water

Put the bones and meaty bits in a stock pot with the onion, celery, carrots, organ meat (if using), and apple cider vinegar. Add the filtered water.

Let the broth mixture sit for 30 minutes, during which time many beneficial minerals will leach from the bones. Turn the heat to high and bring the broth to a boil. It takes around 15 minutes.

Immediately skim all the foamy scum off the top and reduce the heat to low. Cover the pot and simmer the broth for 8 hours or overnight.

Using a strainer, strain the broth into a large bowl. Transfer the cooled, strained broth to covered containers and refrigerate. We use 4 quart-size mason jars or gallon-size covered plastic containers. This will keep up to a month in the refrigerator or 6 months in the freezer.

- -

Note: In a pinch, you can buy premade bone broth and stock (just read the ingredients to make sure there is no gluten).

- -

Fast and Furious II: A Tale of Two Stocks

Stock 1: Slow Cooker Weed Stock

Yields 4 to 6 servings

If you want to get your kids talking about this stock, throw in some chicken feet! They add collagen, which is great for skin and joints. They can be hard to find, but Asian markets and local farmers often have them available.

- 1 to 2 (4- to 5-pound) whole chickens or 1 (5-pound) chuck roast
- 4 chicken feet or 3 marrow bones (optional)
- 4 carrots, cut into 1-inch pieces
- 2 stalks celery, cut into 1-inch pieces
- 1 (16-ounce) bag frozen broccoli, green beans, or lima beans (optional)
- 2 onions, quartered, or several chopped green onions
- 1 potato per person
- 2 garlic cloves, crushed and chopped
- 2 to 3 tablespoons Weed! Herb Mix *(page 74)*
- Filtered water, as needed
- 1 tablespoon apple cider vinegar

Place the chickens or chuck roast, chicken feet or marrow bones (if using), carrots, celery, broccoli, green beans, or lima beans, onions or green onions, garlic, and Weed! Herb Mix in the slow cooker. Add enough filtered water to fill the slow cooker within 2 inches of the rim. Add the apple cider vinegar. Cook on low for 8 to 12 hours.

Eat and enjoy the meat and vegetables. Then, using a strainer, strain the stock into a large bowl. Transfer the strained stock to 1 gallon-size or 4 quart-size glass or plastic covered containers. Refrigerate and enjoy for the next few weeks or freeze for up to 6 months.

Stock 2: Vegetable Stock

Yields 4 to 6 servings

Vegetable stock is homey, comforting, and great for hearty winter soups. It's also very inexpensive and easy to make!

- 8 cups vegetables and/or vegetable trimmings*
- 2 carrots
- 2 stalks celery
- 1 onion
- 1 gallon filtered water
- 1 teaspoon turmeric
- 1 teaspoon curry powder
- 1 teaspoon paprika
- 1 teaspoon pepper
- 1 teaspoon salt

Put the vegetable mixture, carrots, celery, onion, filtered water, turmeric, curry powder, paprika, pepper, and salt in a large stock pot or slow cooker.

If making the stock on the stove, bring the stock to a boil then reduce the heat and simmer, covered, for 6 hours. If using a slow cooker, cook on low overnight or for 6 to 8 hours.

Let the stock cool and, using a strainer, strain the stock into a large bowl. Transfer the strained stock to 1 gallon-size or 4 quart-size glass or plastic covered containers. Refrigerates for a few weeks. Enjoy in soups.

---

*When cutting the ends off carrots, spinach, kale, onions, and other vegetables, I save these washed ends and put them in a gallon-size plastic zip-top bag in the fridge. When the bag is full, it's time to make Vegetable Stock (freeze the bag of trimmings if it will take you more than a few days to fill it up).

Cup o' Breakfast Broth

Yields 4 to 6 servings

The best way to start your day!

- 2 cups Slow Cooker Weed Stock *(page 60)* or Vegetable Stock *(page 61)*
- 2 to 3 cups filtered water
- Garlic powder, to taste
- Onion powder, to taste
- Salt and pepper, to taste
- 1 egg per person (optional)

Heat the stock, filtered water, garlic powder, onion powder, and salt and pepper in a medium saucepan over medium-high heat.

If using the egg, crack the egg into a measuring cup to ensure that it's good. Next, make sure the stock is hot enough to cook the egg. Gently drop the egg into the stock and cook for 3 minutes.

Note: Straws are incredible inventions for compromised children. Every child loves to drink from a straw!

Pho So Simple Soup

Yields 4 to 6 servings

Make this super simple soup when you're sick.

- 2 cups Slow Cooker Weed Stock or Vegetable Stock
- 2 cups filtered water
- 2 green onions, finely chopped
- 1 cup spinach or bok choy, coarsely chopped
- ½ cup mung bean sprouts (optional)
- Salt, to taste

Put the stock, filtered water, green onions, spinach or bok choy, bean sprouts (if using), and salt in a large pot. Cook, covered, over medium heat for 20 to 30 minutes. Serve hot.

Potato and Onion Frittata

Yields 4 to 6 servings

A surprise use for stock!

- 1 large potato, cut into ½-inch pieces
- 1 large onion, cut into ½-inch pieces
- 1 garlic clove, finely chopped
- 5 eggs
- 1 cup room-temperature broth or stock (any variety)
- Salt and pepper, to taste

Preheat the oven to 350°F. Grease a 9-inch pie dish with coconut oil or red palm oil.

In a medium skillet over medium heat, sauté the potato, onion, and garlic until the potato is softened and the onion and garlic are light golden brown. Set the potato mixture aside to cool.

Crack the eggs into a large bowl and stir. Add the stock or broth, potato mixture, and salt and pepper, stirring to combine.

Pour the egg mixture into the pie dish. Bake the frittata for 20 to 30 minutes. Make sure the egg mixture is not totally set and there's just a little liquid on top when you remove it from the oven. Overcooked frittata is horrible and the stock seems to prevent this.

Frittata with a Purpose

Yields 4 to 6 servings

This frittata shines with potato, spinach, broccoli, onion, and greens!

- ¶ 5 eggs
- ¶ 1 cup room-temperature broth or stock (any variety)
- ¶ 1 cup leftover Glamorous Greens Detox *(page 76)*
- ¶ Salt and pepper, to taste

Preheat the oven to 350°F. Grease a 9-inch pie dish.

Crack the eggs into a large bowl and stir. Add the stock or broth, Glamorous Greens, and salt and pepper, stirring to combine.

Pour the egg mixture into the pie dish. Bake the frittata for 20 to 30 minutes. Make sure the egg mixture is not totally set and there's just a little liquid on top when you remove it from the oven. Overcooked frittata is horrible and the stock seems to prevent this.

Super Nitric Oxide Garlic Pea Soup

Yields 4 to 6 servings

Behold the power of good! This is a family favorite.[14]

- 3 cups chicken stock
- 3 cups filtered water
- 1 carrot, coarsely chopped
- 1 (16-ounce) package frozen peas
- 1 cup coarsely chopped kale
- 2 leeks, coarsely chopped
- 3 garlic bulbs (preferably roasted), skins removed
- ½ teaspoon dried thyme
- ½ teaspoon dried oregano
- Salt, to taste
- ½ pound cooked and crispy beef bacon, finely chopped for garnish (optional)

Put the chicken stock, filtered water, carrot, peas, kale, leeks, garlic, thyme, oregano, and salt in a large pot. Cook, covered, over medium heat for 30 minutes, or until the vegetables are soft.

Use an immersion blender to blend the soup to the desired consistency. Alternatively, allow the soup to cool slightly, then blend it in a high-speed blender (in batches, if necessary).

Serve garnished with chopped crispy bacon for a real bonus!

---

14   J. O. Lundberg, E. Weitzberg, and M. T. Gladwin, "The Nitrate-Nitrite-Nitric Oxide Pathway in Physiology and Therapeutics," *Nature Reviews Drug Discovery* 7, no. 2 (February 2008): 156–167; R. M. Palmer, D. S. Ashton, and S. Moncada, "Vascular Endothelial Cells Synthesize Nitric Oxide from L-Arginine," *Nature* 333, no. 6174 (June 16, 1988): 664–666.

Cabbage Soup

Yields 4 to 6 servings

Supplements for reflux and stomach pain often include the ingredients of cabbage or okra, so enjoy this tasty way to help your tummy.

- 2 cups stock (any variety)
- 2 cups filtered water
- 1 small head green cabbage, chopped into ½-inch pieces
- 1 cup fresh okra (optional)
- 1 medium potato, chopped into ½-inch pieces
- 1 large carrot, chopped into ½-inch pieces
- Salt and pepper, to taste
- ½ pound cooked grass-fed hamburger or ground poultry (optional)

Put the stock and filtered water in a large pot. Add the cabbage, okra (if using), potato, carrot, salt and pepper, and hamburger or ground poultry (if using). Cover and cook over medium heat for 30 minutes, or until the vegetables are tender. Serve hot.

Tom Kha Gai (Coconut Soup)

Yields 4 to 6 servings

This is the all-time favorite soup in my family.

- 3 cups chicken stock (or stock of choice)
- 2 cups filtered water
- 1 large carrot, cut into ¼-inch thick slices
- 3 green onions, finely chopped
- 2 garlic cloves, finely chopped
- 1 medium green bell pepper, thinly sliced
- 1 (1-inch) knob fresh ginger, grated
- 1 tablespoon fresh or bottled lemon juice
- 1 teaspoon lemongrass paste and a full stem of lemongrass
- 1 teaspoon dried thyme
- 1 teaspoon dried oregano
- 1 teaspoon curry powder
- Red pepper flakes, to taste
- Salt, to taste
- Coconut oil, as needed
- ½ pound leftover cooked chicken or uncooked chicken strips, cut into bite-size pieces
- 1 ½ cups or 1 (15-ounce) can full-fat coconut milk
- Fresh cilantro, chopped, for topping

Put the chicken stock and filtered water in a large pot. Add the carrot, green onions, garlic, bell pepper, ginger, lemon juice, lemongrass, thyme, oregano, curry powder, red pepper flakes, and salt. Cover and cook over medium heat for 30 minutes, or until the vegetables are tender.

While the soup is cooking, heat some coconut oil in a medium skillet over medium heat. Sauté the chicken pieces for about 10 minutes, until golden brown. Now add the cooked chicken pieces and the coconut milk to the soup. Cook the soup for an additional 5 to 10 minutes. Garnish with the fresh cilantro and serve.

Tomato Soup

Yields 4 to 6 servings

This soup works for us when head colds or headaches strike.

- 2 cups stock (any variety)
- 2 cups filtered water
- 4 large tomatoes, quartered
- 1 garlic clove, minced
- ¼ large onion, chopped
- 1 teaspoon dried basil
- 1 teaspoon dried oregano
- 1 teaspoon dried thyme
- Salt and pepper, to taste
- Homemade GFCF Yogurt *(page 35)*

Put the stock, filtered water, tomatoes, garlic, onion, basil, oregano, thyme, and salt and pepper in a large pot. Cover and cook over medium heat for 30 minutes.

Use an immersion blender and blend until the soup reaches the desired consistency. Alternatively, allow the soup to cool slightly, then blend it in a high-speed blender (in batches, if necessary).

Serve the soup topped with a dollop of Homemade GFCF Yogurt.

Chapter 9: Not-So-Forbidden Fruits and Veggies

There's a mountain of studies confirming the health benefits of fruits and vegetables, particularly leafy greens and cruciferous vegetables such as cabbage, cauliflower, and broccoli. They are rich in Indole-3-carbinol (I3C), which protects cells against cancerous changes via DNA damage.[15] Kale, bok choy, and mustard greens, too, are all full of fiber, vitamins, and minerals that protect us from heart disease and diabetes.

---

15   Maria Traka et al., "Broccoli Consumption Interacts with *GSTM1* to Perturb Oncogenic Signalling Pathways in the Prostate," *PLoS ONE* 3, no. 7 (2008): e2568, doi:10.1371/journal.pone.0002568.

The Case for Greens

There's no doubt: it's proven that green leafy vegetables are most protective against coronary heart disease and ischemic stroke risk, as well as many other health indications. They are high in L-arginine, which converts to nitric oxide[16] and hosts a variety of benefits to a compromised body.[17] These vegetables also contain folate. It is a natural source of folic acid and will help your body recover. My hope is that by using the yummy recipes in this real-food GFCF cookbook, kids and adults alike will learn to love this most absorbable form of nutrients.

Whenever possible, choose local, non-genetically modified, and organic produce. Nutrient levels are higher when the produce is fresh. If organic produce in the supermarket is too expensive, a more affordable option is going to a farmer's market. You might have to ask around, but inevitably there is a vendor who is supportive and holistically minded. To find a market in your area, visit www.localharvest.org/farmers-markets.

---

16   See note 10.

17   N. G. Hord, Y. Tang, and N. S. Bryan, "Food Sources of Nitrates and Nitrites: The Physiologic Context for Potential Health Benefits," *American Journal of Clinical Nutrition* 90, no. 1 (July 2009): 1–10, doi: 10.3945/ajcn.2008.27131.

Mom to Mom

According to the CDC, many of the adolescent population eats less than one fruit or vegetable per day.[18]

We are changing this with our kids. Most of our minerals and vitamins come through these real-food sources. And it is much easier than taking a pill.

Fostering many children and working with some orphan homes, we find that some of the children have histamine or glutamate issues aggravated by broths and stocks. These children have really compromised guts. Hives and eczema are the most prevalent symptoms we have faced after consuming broth. We generally start juicing and have a lot of success mixing up the vegetables so we don't have too much of any one vegetable. With this variety of vegetables, it helps us make sure there are not too many salicylates, oxalates, propionates (organic helps here), rubiscolin, and natural nitrates (celery). One child may have a sensitivity to oxalates, whereas another child is sensitive to salicylates. Therefore, to make this affordable and manageable, we just keep a revolving, seasonal door on the vegetables we use.

Our family's approach is to eat everything in moderation. In the beginning, we used so many carrots that we all started turning orange! At first, it looked nice like a tan, but it got super orange and scary. So we learned to mix it up, using many different veggies and fruits and utilizing their different valuable minerals.

Along with a great holistic doctor, a good resource for more information is www.failsafediet.com.

—Mandy

---

18   National Center for Chronic Disease Prevention and Health Promotion, *State Indicator Report on Fruits and Vegetables 2013* (Atlanta: Centers for Disease Control and Prevention, 2013).

Weed! Herb Mix

Yields about 2 ½ cups of seasoning

Everything tastes better with spice! Make this seasoning mix with dried and/or fresh herbs.

- 3 tablespoons salt
- 3 tablespoons turmeric
- 6 tablespoons paprika
- 6 tablespoons curry powder
- 6 tablespoons fresh or dried thyme
- 6 tablespoons fresh or dried oregano
- 6 tablespoons fresh or dried basil
- 6 tablespoons fresh or dried sage

Mix together the salt, turmeric, paprika, curry powder, thyme, oregano, basil and sage in a small glass or plastic container. (If using fresh chopped herbs, store the seasoning in the refrigerator and it will be good for a week in a plastic bag.) Use 1 to 2 tablespoons for every dish!

Chelating Cilantro Rice

Yields 4 to 6 servings

Cilantro is a food that helps move out metals.[19]

- 1 bunch fresh cilantro, coarsely chopped
- ½ cup fresh parsley, coarsely chopped
- 2 medium tomatoes, chopped into ½-inch pieces, or 1/3 cup spaghetti sauce
- ½ medium onion, chopped into ½-inch pieces
- 2 garlic cloves, minced, or 1 tablespoon jarred minced garlic
- 2 cups uncooked white or brown rice
- 2 cups chicken or beef stock
- 2 cups filtered water

Put the cilantro, parsley, tomatoes or spaghetti sauce, onion, garlic, rice, chicken or beef stock, and filtered water in a large pot. Bring the mixture to a boil, reduce to a simmer, and cook 30 minutes. Enjoy!

---

19   See note 7; Y. Omura et al., "Significant Mercury Deposits in Internal Organs Following the Removal of Dental Amalgam, and Development of Pre-Cancer on the Gingiva and the Sides of the Tongue and Their Represented Organs as a Result of Inadvertent Exposure to Strong Curing Light (Used to Solidify Synthetic Dental Filling Material) and Effective Treatment: A Clinical Case Report, Along with Organ Representation Areas for Each Tooth," *Acupuncture and Electro-Therapeutics Research* 21, no. 2 (April–June 1996): 133–160; K. B. Ewan and R. Pamphlett, "Increased Inorganic Mercury in Spinal Motor Neurons Following Chelating Agents," *Neurotoxicology* 17, no. 2 (Summer 1996): 343–349; C. W. Cha, "A Study on the Effect of Garlic to the Heavy Metal Poisoning of Rat," *Journal of Korean Medical Science* 2, no. 4 (December 1987): 213–224; see note 8.

Glamorous Greens Detox

Yields 4 to 6 servings

This dish keeps the pathways and arteries flowing.[20]

- 1 tablespoon leftover chicken fat from stock, coconut oil, or ghee
- 1 teaspoon turmeric
- 1 teaspoon curry powder
- 1 teaspoon dried thyme
- 1 teaspoon dried oregano
- 1 teaspoon paprika
- 1 teaspoon salt
- 2 medium sweet or white potatoes, cut into ½-inch pieces
- 1 medium onion, chopped into ½-inch pieces
- 1 garlic clove, minced
- 1 bunch (10 ounces) kale, chopped into bite-size pieces
- 1 bunch (10 ounces) spinach, chopped into bite-size pieces
- 1 bunch (10 ounces) bok choy, chopped into bite-size pieces
- 1 bunch (10 ounces) napa cabbage, chopped into bite-size pieces
- 1 cup chopped eggplant (½-inch pieces; optional)

In a very large skillet over medium heat, add the chicken fat, coconut oil, or ghee, turmeric, curry powder, thyme, oregano, paprika, and salt. (If you are missing a spice or two, just make it without those or replace with your favorite.) Add the potatoes, onion, and garlic and sauté for about 10 minutes.

Add the kale, spinach, bok choy, and napa cabbage. Sauté until the greens wilt and become a little darker green. (Don't cook them to death, though!) Serve warm.

Remember to save any leftovers for an amazing frittata the next morning (see Potato and Onion Frittata *(page 64)* and Frittata with a Purpose *(page 65)*).

---

20   See note 10.

Papaya Pepper

Yields ½ cup

OK, adult talk here. This stuff eradicates intestinal parasites.[21] Yes, we all have them—it's basic biology. Papaya seeds actually attack only the bad bugs, which makes it an awesome condiment. Incorporating this into your diet has got to be helpful!

- 1 small papaya (the smaller variety has more seeds)
- 1 tablespoon salt

Gather all the seeds from the papaya and put them on a baking sheet. (Be sure to enjoy the fruit fresh or freeze it for a shake.)

Spread the seeds on a baking sheet and sprinkle with the salt.

Preheat the oven to 170°F.

Place the papaya seeds in the oven and bake for 4 to 5 hours. When they are done, they will look like hard, crinkled peppercorns.

I put them in a pepper grinder, but you could put in them a coffee grinder or crush them between two spoons. I use this instead of standard black pepper and sprinkle it on any dish.

---

21   J. A. Okeniyi et al., "Effectiveness of Dried Carica Papaya Seeds Against Human Intestinal Parasitosis: A Pilot Study," *Journal of Medicinal Food* 10, no. 1 (March 2007): 194–196.

Browned Brussels Sprouts with Apple

Yields 4 to 6 servings

For many, Brussels sprouts are too bitter to enjoy, especially when boiled. But something magical happens when you cut them in half and sauté them in a skillet.

- 1 pound fresh Brussels sprouts
- 1 tablespoon chicken fat from stock, ghee, or coconut oil
- 1 large apple of choice, chopped into small cubes
- Salt, to taste

Wash the Brussels sprouts well and cut them in half. Melt the fat, ghee, or coconut oil in a skillet over medium heat and sauté the Brussels sprouts and apple for around 10 minutes. Season with salt to taste.

Roasted Potatoes and Avocado

Yields 4 to 6 servings

The creaminess of avocados pairs beautifully with the starchiness of potatoes. Delish!

- 3 white potatoes, unpeeled and cut into wedges
- 3 sweet potatoes-, peeled and cut into wedges
- 1/3 cup coconut oil or ghee
- Salt and Papaya Pepper to taste *(page 77)*
- 2 avocados, pitted, peeled, and cut into ½-inch thick slices

Preheat the oven to 325°F.

Spread the white potatoes and sweet potatoes on a baking sheet.

Melt the coconut oil or ghee and pour it over the potatoes. Season with salt and Papaya Pepper to taste and bake for 30 to 45 minutes.

Remove the potatoes from the oven, add the avocados, and bake for another 5 minutes. Alternatively, simply add the avocados and serve.

Easy Baked Onion

Yields 1 serving

Onions become amazingly sweet and tender when they're baked. I'm sure you'll enjoy this recipe!

- 1 Vidalia onion per person
- Coconut oil or red palm oil, as needed

Preheat the oven to 300°F.

Cut the root end off the onion and peel the skin off.

Rub a little coconut oil or red palm oil on the onion and place it in a shallow baking dish.

Bake the onion for 2 hours or until softened.

Eat with a knife and fork. Perfection!

Butternut Squash Bake

Yields 4 to 6 servings

This simple recipe is surprisingly delicious!

- ⵌ 1 medium butternut squash, peeled, seeded, and cut into 1-inch cubes
- ⵌ 1 large onion, chopped into ½-inch pieces
- ⵌ 2 tablespoons melted coconut oil, ghee, or schmaltz (chicken fat)
- ⵌ Salt and Papaya Pepper to taste *(page 77)*

Preheat the oven to 325°F.

Spread the squash and onion on a baking sheet. Drizzle the coconut oil, ghee, or schmaltz over the vegetables and season with salt and Papaya Pepper to taste.

Bake for 1 hour or until soft.

(Squash) Spaghetti

Yields 4 to 6 servings

This Italian favorite is now a whole-food recipe made deliciously simple.

- 1 large spaghetti squash
- Coconut oil, as needed
- 1 (16-ounce) jar spaghetti sauce
- 1 (10-ounce) bunch spinach or kale
- Salt and pepper, to taste

Optional meat-sauce version:

- ½ pound grass-fed hamburger
- 1 medium onion
- 3 tablespoons liver pâté

Preheat the oven to 300°F. Wash the spaghetti squash, rub it all over with a bit of coconut oil, and place it in a baking pan. Bake for 1 hour if it is large or 30 minutes if it is small. Remove the squash from the oven and let it cool.

While the squash is cooling, heat the spaghetti sauce and spinach or kale in a medium saucepan over medium heat until hot.

If preparing the meat-sauce version, heat a medium skillet over medium heat and cook the hamburger, onion, and pâté for about 15 minutes. Once the hamburger is cooked, add the spaghetti sauce and spinach.

Cut the squash open and remove the seeds from the center. Use a fork to pull the noodle-like squash out onto dinner plates. Season with salt and pepper and top with the spaghetti sauce or meat sauce.

Better than the pasta version!

Glamorous Green Juice and Apple Juice

Yields 4 to 6 servings

A scrumptious detoxing green drink.

- 2 (10-ounce) bunches bok choy
- 5 ounces romaine lettuce
- 1 (10-ounce) bunch spinach
- 1 (1-inch) knob fresh ginger
- 2 cups apple juice or Fizztacular Apple Soda Pop *(page 131)*
- Melted coconut oil, for serving

Blend the bok choy, romaine, spinach, ginger, and apple juice or Fizztacular Apple Soda Pop in a high-speed blender until smooth. Alternatively, juice the bok choy, romaine, spinach, and ginger in a juicer, then add the apple juice or Apple Soda.

If you used a blender to process the greens and ginger, put a strainer in a large bowl and pour the green juice through.

Add 1 tablespoon of the pulp back to the juice with a bit of melted coconut oil. Stir and serve. Cheers!

Easy Cauliflower Bake

Yields 4 to 6 servings

And I mean *easy*!

- 1 medium head cauliflower
- 1 tablespoon coconut oil or ghee
- ½ teaspoon curry powder
- ½ teaspoon turmeric
- ½ teaspoon salt
- Olive oil, for drizzling

Preheat the oven to 350°F.

Rub the coconut oil or ghee around the whole head of cauliflower. Rub the curry powder, turmeric, and salt into the oil to coat the cauliflower. Place the head of cauliflower in a shallow baking dish, uncovered, and bake for 30 to 40 minutes. Remove the cauliflower from the oven and drizzle with olive oil. Chop the cauliflower head into individual helpings and serve.

Roasted Cauliflower Rice

Yields 4 to 6 servings

Try this tasty alternative to rice and get a kick of cruciferous nutrition!

- 1 head Easy Cauliflower Bake *(page 84)*

Cut the cauliflower head into small pieces and pulse them in a blender or food processor for 5 to 10 seconds to create an amazing rice-like base for soups and other dishes.

Watermelon Shake

Yields 4 to 6 servings

To help prevent heart disease and sunburn, try to eat foods high in lycopene, like watermelon, tomato paste, and cabbage.[22]

- 2 to 3 cups watermelon chunks
- ½ cup Homemade GFCF Yogurt *(page 35)*
- Ice cubes, as needed

Blend the watermelon, yogurt, and ice cubes in a high-speed blender.

Tasty heart medicine and sunscreen!

---

22   M. Rizwan et al., "Tomato Paste Rich in Lycopene Protects Against Cutaneous Photodamage in Humans in Vivo: A Randomized Controlled Trial," *British Journal of Dermatology* 164, no. 1 (January 2011): 154–164, doi:10.1111/j.1365-2133.2010.10057.x; Aruna Poduri et al., "*Citrullus lantus* 'Sentinel' (watermelon) Extract Reduces Atherosclerosis in LDL Receptor Deficient Mice," *Journal of Nutritional Biochemistry* 24, no. 5 (May 2013): 882–886, doi:dx.doi.org/10.1016/j.jnutbio.2012.05.011.

Sautéed Beets and Onion

Yields 4 to 6 servings

This recipe offers gallbladder support[23] and is such a beautiful color!

- 1 tablespoon coconut oil, schmaltz, or ghee
- 6 large red beets, peeled and coarsely chopped
- 1 large onion, peeled and chopped into ½-inch pieces
- Salt and garlic powder, to taste

Heat the coconut oil, schmaltz, or ghee in a medium skillet over medium heat. Add the beets and onion. Sauté the vegetables for 15 to 25 minutes, until they are soft and sweet. Season to taste with the salt and garlic powder. Serve warm.

---

23   See note 10; Govind J. Kapadia et al., "Cytotoxic Effect of the Red Beetroot (Beta vulgaris L.) Extract Compared to Doxorubicin (Adriamycin) in the Human Prostate (PC-3) and Breast (MCF-7) Cancer Cell Lines," *Anti-Cancer Agents in Medicinal Chemistry* 11, no. 3 (March 2011): 280–284.

Carcinogen Bustin' Broccoli and Rice

Yields 4 to 6 servings

You are getting the swing of it! Bust those carcinogens with broccoli![24]

- 3 cups chicken or beef stock
- 3 cups filtered water
- 1 to 2 cups uncooked brown, white, or red rice
- 2 cups chopped broccoli or broccoli sprouts
- Salt, to taste

Put the chicken or beef stock, filtered water, rice, broccoli, and salt in a large pot. (If you are using broccoli sprouts, stir them in after the rice is cooked.) Bring to a boil over medium-high heat, then simmer on low for 30 minutes, or until the rice is cooked. Ladle into bowls and serve.

---

24   See note 11.

Starring Apple and Sweet Potato Bake

Yields 4 to 6 servings

A terrific treat with stars (if you cut it right)!

- 2 large apples (any variety), sliced ¼-inch thick according to the instructions below
- 2 to 3 medium sweet potatoes, peeled and sliced ¼-inch thick
- ½ cup full-fat coconut milk
- 2 teaspoons ground cinnamon

Preheat the oven to 300°F. Grease an 8 x 8-inch baking dish or a 9 x 5-inch loaf pan with coconut oil.

Hold the stem of the apple and turn the apple on its side. Rather than cutting wedges, and leaving the core, slice across the core into circles as shown in the photo. Each slice will have a star shape in the center!

Place the apples and sweet potatoes in the prepared baking dish or loaf pan. Pour the coconut milk on top and sprinkle with the cinnamon. Bake the apples and sweet potatoes for 40 minutes, until the potatoes are soft.

Cleansing Salad

Yields 4 to 6 servings

Whip that stomach bug and get back on your feet!

- 1 large head iceberg lettuce
- 2 large carrots, shredded
- 2 avocados, pitted, peeled, and sliced ½-inch thick
- 4 ounces Probiotic Salad Dressing *(page 134)*
- Salt and Papaya Pepper to taste *(page 77)*

Cut the head of lettuce into 6 wedges and place them on plates. Sprinkle the shredded carrot on top of the lettuce wedges, top with the avocado slices, and drizzle with the Probiotic Salad Dressing. Season with salt and Papaya Pepper to taste.

Chapter 10: Majestic Meat

An important goal of *Real Food Recovery* is to minimize the eating of foods that have been altered, mishandled, or mistreated. It is more important to eat a modest amount of healthy, high-quality meat rather than loads of cheap meat that comes from animals who are not nourished or treated well.

Meat and Money

With regard to preparing meat, it is well studied that cooking *low and slow* is the healthiest way to go about it. For instance, the University of Minnesota reported that women who ate overcooked hamburgers had a 50 percent greater risk of breast cancer than women who ate rare or medium hamburgers.[25] Whoa! Pink in the middle, please.

Beneficial foods come at a higher price, but, then, so do conventional medicines and side effects. It is necessary to evaluate what something *really* costs before we eat it. So, if eating quality meat on a regular basis is not working for your budget, eat less meat and integrate more delicious veggie recipes into your repertoire!

Our family found that locating a local farmer (ideally, an organically minded one) allows us to buy meat in bulk for more affordable prices. Many buy the whole, half, or quarter of a cow and freeze it for the year. This allows you to get the bones and organs, which is discussed next.

There are many nations who eat organ meat as much as meat tissue. The United States population has generally lost this benefit! Make a genuine effort to incorporate this beneficial food—there are reasons it is historically and globally appreciated. Try to camouflage it in ground meat or purchase it in supplement form.

Here are tremendous resources to help you find better meat, eggs, and more in your local area: www.eatwild.com/products/index.html and www.westonaprice.org.

A Word on Liver

Liver is a nutrient-dense food filled with vitamins A and D (found in poultry only) and is our best source for vitamins B12 and B6. Liver also has antioxidants, copper, iron, and zinc. If you can find ways to add liver to your burgers, stocks, and meatloaf, it is the ultimate secret weapon in supporting a body. Try "hiding" it in your favorite dishes—this way, it "disappears" into your familiar recipes, and the benefits will greatly outweigh any effort (or hesitation).

In fact, liver pâté is making a real comeback in the United States, as is the fatted liver of a duck or goose called foie gras. Organ meat is much more common in countries outside of the United States. But if you can't get past the thought of eating an organ, purchase glandulars or liver in supplement form to benefit your health.

---

25   Wei Zheng et al., "Well-Done Meat Intake and the Risk of Breast Cancer," *Journal of the National Cancer Institute* 90, no. 22 (November 18, 1998): 1724–1729.

Mom to Mom

Each child we fostered had some significant health issue. When we finally got to adopt, we faced a host of new challenges: babies born with drugs in their system suffer in many unique ways. Somewhere along the way, our family began to incorporate liver pâté and other organs.

Miraculously, we discovered early on that incorporating organ meat into a few meals a week had super benefits for us all. We notice a marked improvement in just two months with the diet we maintain.

The child we adopted is thriving! And we are proud to say that the children we did not get to adopt certainly left us in restored health with a better disposition before returning to their biological parents.

So as foreign as organ meat might seem, we encourage you to power through and give it a try.

I think you will be pleasantly surprised at the benefits to your health. Just keep the organ meat around 30 percent of the total meat used and you can't taste it!

—Mandy

Super Beef Burgers

Yields 4 to 6 servings

These burgers are simple, fast, and delicious!

- 2 pounds grass-fed hamburger
- 1 tablespoon salt
- 2 quarts filtered water
- 1 tablespoon garlic salt
- 1 teaspoon pepper
- 1 teaspoon paprika
- 1 onion, chopped into ¼-inch pieces and sautéed
- ¼ cup chopped fresh basil or 2 teaspoons dried basil
- 1 cup grass-fed blended cow or chicken liver (optional)

Soak the hamburger in the salt and water for 30 minutes in a large bowl and rinse. (It's a quick way to clean the meat. Plus, the flavor is much better.)

Mix the hamburger, garlic salt, pepper, paprika, onion, basil, and liver (if using) in a large bowl to combine. Take a large handful of hamburger (about ½ cup) and form 6 patties that are approximately 4 inches across and ½-inch thick.

Sauté the hamburger patties in a medium skillet over medium heat until they are slightly pink inside.

Enjoy and be nourished!

Best Slow Cooker Brisket

Yields 4 to 6 servings

This recipe is a great summertime dish—the slow cooker keeps your kitchen cool and comfortable.

- 1 (3- to 4-pound) brisket
- 2 cups beef or vegetable stock
- 3 to 4 large leeks, cut into ¼-inch thick slices
- 1 garlic bulb, peeled and cloves roughly chopped
- 2 tablespoons organic, gluten-free tamari sauce
- 1 teaspoon dried mustard
- 1 teaspoon salt
- 1 teaspoon ground coriander seeds

Sear the brisket in a large greased skillet over high heat for 5 minutes per side.

Place the brisket in the slow cooker, fat-side up, so it can drip flavor into the meat.

Add the stock, leeks, garlic, tamari, mustard, salt, and coriander seed. Cook on low for 6 to 8 hours.

Bon appétit!

Hamburger Soup

Yields 6 to 10 servings

Delicious soup that stretches the meat for several meals!

- 1 pound grass-fed hamburger
- 1 pound grass-fed ground lamb (or another pound of hamburger)
- 1 medium onion, cut into ½-inch pieces
- ½ cup liver pâté (optional)
- 3 garlic cloves, roughly chopped
- 1 (10-ounce) bunch spinach, chopped to bite-size pieces
- 1 tablespoon turmeric
- 1 tablespoon curry powder
- 8 cups filtered water
- 1 cup broth (optional)

Place the hamburger, lamb or additional hamburger, and onion in the slow cooker. Cook for 2 hours on low.

Chop up the hamburger mixture with a wooden spoon and add the pâté (if using), garlic, spinach, turmeric, curry powder, filtered water, and broth (optional). Cook on high for 3 hours or on low for 8 hours.

Super Beef Meatloaf

Yields 4 to 6 servings

This meatloaf is the ultimate comfort food!

- 2 pounds grass-fed hamburger
- 1 tablespoon salt
- 2 quarts filtered water
- ½ cup blended beef or chicken liver or liver pâté (optional)
- 1 tablespoon garlic salt
- 1 teaspoon pepper
- 1 teaspoon paprika
- 1 medium onion, finely chopped and sautéed
- 1/4 cup chopped fresh basil or parsley
- ½ (16-ounce) jar spaghetti sauce

Soak the hamburger in the salt and filtered water for 30 minutes and rinse. (It's a quick way to clean the meat. Plus, the flavor is much better.)

Preheat the oven to 350°F.

In a large bowl, mix together the hamburger, liver or liver pâté, garlic salt, pepper, paprika, onion, and basil or parsley.

Transfer the mixture to a 9 x 5-inch loaf pan and pat down to smooth the top. Pour the spaghetti sauce over the meatloaf and bake for 40 minutes or until medium with a little pink in the middle.

Chili

Yields 4 to 6 servings

Enjoy this chili after a long day at work or after coming in from the cold. It never fails to warm you up!

- 1 pound grass-fed hamburger
- 1 medium onion, chopped into ½-inch pieces
- 1 (10-ounce) bag frozen lima beans
- 1 (15-ounce) can garbanzo beans or 2 cups soaked beans *(page 112)*
- 1 (10-ounce) bunch spinach, chopped into ½-inch pieces
- 2 tablespoons chili powder
- 1 tablespoon ground cumin
- 2 garlic cloves, minced
- 2 cups tomato sauce
- 1 cup filtered water
- 1 cup chopped tomatoes
- Salt, to taste

Place the hamburger, onion, lima beans, garbanzo beans, spinach, chili powder, cumin, garlic, tomato sauce, filtered water, chopped tomatoes, and salt in the slow cooker. Cover and cook for 8 hours.

Crusted Chicken

Yields 4 to 6 servings

You might want to double this. Just sayin'.

- ¶ 1/3 cup ghee or coconut oil (or a combination)
- ¶ 4 large chicken breasts (about 4 pounds)
- ¶ 1 teaspoon turmeric
- ¶ 1 teaspoon dried oregano
- ¶ 1 teaspoon dried thyme
- ¶ 1 teaspoon dried basil

Heat the ghee or coconut oil in a medium skillet over medium heat. Place the chicken breasts in the skillet, skin-side down. Sprinkle the turmeric, oregano, thyme, and basil over the breasts.

Cook about 10 minutes on each side until the breasts are golden and cooked throughout and the skin is crispy.

Farmer Susan's Herb-Orange Chicken

Yields 4 to 6 servings

This recipe comes from a produce farmer like no other. We have enjoyed learning from her. Thank you, Susan!

- 1 sprig fresh rosemary or 1 tablespoon dried rosemary
- 1 (4- to 5-pound) whole chicken or 4 pounds chicken thighs
- 1 cup fresh orange juice or lemon juice
- ½ cup coconut oil
- 4 medium potatoes, quartered
- 1 tablespoon paprika
- Salt and pepper, to taste

Stuff the rosemary into the cavity of the whole chicken. If using chicken thighs, simply place the rosemary in the slow cooker. Place the chicken or chicken thighs, orange or lemon juice, coconut oil, potatoes, paprika, and salt and pepper in the slow cooker. Cook on low for 6 to 8 hours.

Slow Cooker Chicken Marinade

Yields 4 to 6 servings

Melt-in-your-mouth chicken!

- 1 (4- to 5-pound) whole chicken
- 1 cup Olive Oil Salad Dressing *(page 123)*
- 1 (10-ounce) bag frozen vegetables (such as field peas or lima beans)
- 1 cup filtered water
- Paprika, to taste
- 3 to 4 sprigs fresh thyme and 3 to 4 sprigs sage, stuffed inside the chicken cavity

Place the chicken in the slow cooker and pour the Salad Dressing over it. Empty the bag of frozen vegetables around the chicken and sprinkle the paprika on top. Add the filtered water and cover. Cook on low for 4 to 6 hours.

Wild-Winged Slow Chicken

Yields 4 to 6 servings

These wings are simple, budget friendly, and delicious!

- 1 pound chicken wings
- ¼ cup ghee or coconut oil
- Crushed garlic, to taste
- Salt and pepper, to taste

Wash the chicken under cool running water and pat dry.

Heat the ghee or coconut oil in a large skillet over medium heat. Add the garlic and chicken wings to the skillet, skin-side down. Cook the wings for 15 minutes. Season the wings with salt and pepper to taste, turn and cook another 15 minutes.

Wild Fish: The Brain Food

Yields 4 to 6 servings

Wild-caught fish is such an effective anti-inflammatory agent and source of omega-3 oils. These are beneficial to our brain function while also easing aging and repairing skin disorders.[26]

- Ghee or coconut oil, as needed
- 1 (2-pound) filet wild-caught salmon, haddock, or red snapper
- 1 teaspoon fresh or bottled lemon juice
- Pinch salt

Heat the ghee or coconut oil in a medium skillet over medium heat. Add the salmon filet, then squeeze or pour the lemon juice over the fish. Sprinkle the filet with the salt.

Cook the filet for 5 minutes, then flip and cook another 5 minutes. Remove from the heat as soon as it is flaky and whitish in color.

---

26   Dr. Nicholas Perricone is a board-certified dermatologist. He is a well-respected aging expert and has won awards as an inventor and educator. He has recommended wild-caught salmon for years and is the author of *The Wrinkle Cure*.

Lamb Shank

Yields 4 to 6 servings

This dish is perfect with gluten-free couscous and Glamorous Greens *(page 76)* at the end of a long day.

- 2 lamb shanks
- ¼ cup fresh or bottled lemon juice
- 1 sprig fresh rosemary or 1 tablespoon dried rosemary
- 1 medium onion, cut into ½-inch pieces
- 1 teaspoon dried thyme
- ½ cup coconut oil, melted or solid
- Salt and pepper, to taste

Place the lamb shanks, lemon juice, rosemary, onion, thyme, coconut oil, and salt and pepper in the slow cooker. Cover and cook on low for 6 to 8 hours.

Alternatively, preheat the oven to 350°F. Place the lamb shanks, lemon juice, rosemary, onion, thyme, coconut oil, and salt and pepper in a 12 x 18-inch roasting pan. Roast the shanks in the oven for 1 to 1 ½ hours.

Meatballs

Yields 4 to 6 servings (about 40 meatballs)

These meatballs are wonderful with (Squash) Spaghetti (see index).

- 1 tablespoon avocado oil or schmaltz
- 1 pound ground turkey, lamb, or beef
- 1 small onion, minced and sautéed
- 1 egg
- 1 teaspoon paprika
- ¼ cup chopped fresh herbs (rosemary is great)
- 1 teaspoon salt
- 1/3 cup chicken liver pâté (optional)

Preheat the oven to 300°F and grease a 9 x 11-inch baking dish with the avocado oil or schmaltz.

In a large bowl, mix together the ground turkey, lamb, or beef, onion, egg, paprika, herbs, salt, and chicken liver pâté (if using). Scoop out the meat by tablespoons, roll them into balls, and place them in the baking dish.

Cook the meatballs 40 minutes or until just at medium-well.

Chapter 11: Your Mineral Gold Mine in the Kitchen

Between my children and foster children, my family takes lots of minerals and supplements. I am no stranger to the challenge of getting a special-needs child or someone who doesn't feel strong to ingest so many powders, potions, and pills. Thank goodness for the super-nutritious, mineral-rich vegetables that help us meet our quotas. Please refer to chapter 9 for some delicious vegetable recipes, and whatever you do, don't skimp on the salt!

Please Pass the Salt

Since minerals are about 4 percent of our bodies' makeup, it is uncanny that we do not produce minerals. We are completely dependent upon consuming or absorbing our minerals.

Our muscles, organs, and valves can't function without minerals. And superhero status comes with the right balance of minerals![27]

In addition to stocks and vegetables, colored salt is the most nutrient-dense, with such salts as sel gris (gray salt) or pink Himalayan salt. Unlike bleached white table salt, these beautiful, often hand-farmed colored salts can contain up to—get this—eighty-two trace minerals!

Sure, there are trendy diets that say, "Drop the salt!" But human biochemistry *requires* salt, among other minerals. In fact, there have been periods of history during which salt was traded with a higher value than gold. And I'm willing to bet it wasn't bleached salt!

---

27   "Minerals," Medline Plus, https://www.nlm.nih.gov/medlineplus/minerals.html. Accessed November 2015.

Did you know that animals lick salt blocks full of minerals in order to better digest their foods? Any good farmer can tell you this. Minerals actually reduce the gorging of food because it facilitates the transfer of nutrients more efficiently.

Of course, passing around a salt block at the table might be a bit awkward (if not entertaining), so try this Mineral-Enriched Water. And keep a nice little bowl of lovely colored salt to pinch and sprinkle over the beautiful foods you prepare.

Mineral-Enriched Water

Yields 48 cups (with only 1 to 3 tablespoons needed per cup of water or soup)

Use this water to help your body maintain the delicate balance of trace minerals it needs.

Fill 1 (1-quart) mason jar 1/3 full of mineral-rich colored salt (gray, pink, lava, and so on). Fill the remainder of the jar with filtered water. Screw on the lid and shake.

Let the salt soak for a day, until most of the salt is dissolved. The water has absorbed the minerals to its full capacity and rests in this liquid state. Now you can add minerals to your drinks and soups. It only takes a teaspoon or so per person.

Children and adults that are compromised find there is a general deficiency in minerals, so incorporating these minerals into drinks is extremely beneficial, absorbable, and simple:

Add 1 to 3 teaspoons as desired into a glass of water

Add 1 teaspoon to soups

It's a great addition to any prepared food that needs a bit of salt, because it is easily blended into the entire dish

The taste is similar when you inadvertently swallow water in the ocean while getting pummeled by a wave, but this one is on purpose and in small doses.

Mom to Mom

These days, it's not very popular to work with foster kids or to believe in God, but somehow both found me. Maybe not on purpose, but both found me.

Our first foster-to-adopt son was a two-year-old boy suffering from sheer neglect and abandonment. His biological parents, who knew little of love, were bound by drug addiction and violence. I pledged my heart and soul to save him.

Then, this beautiful being, the very child whom I restored through a good diet, love, and consistency, who began to feel peaceful and safe and to glow with his own amazingness, who let me into his heart, was diagnosed with stage 4 Neuroblastoma cancer in the spinal ganglia. He had apparently had it since birth.

Angry doesn't even come close to what I felt. However, I didn't want to stay in this emotional place, so I started over, from the very beginning. And in my searching, I discovered what would work for me. In this deep place, I decided to be like "salt" for the world—no matter what befell me, I would live in trust and gratitude to a Creator who understands cancer, food, science, and disease much better than I ever will. I am committed to sharing our successes and failures in a place that holds no judgment, in the spirit of families supporting, witnessing, and inspiring each other. I have made so many mistakes in life that I find great joy in just loving, learning, and enjoying people as we are!

We took in many more foster children to adopt and raise equally alongside our biological children, and we faced many diseases and difficulties. We also reached great levels of recovery through much of the real-food, GFCF diet shared in this book. My story is filled with a love that doesn't give up and a hope that never fails.

I genuinely wish this for you also.

—Mandy

Chapter 12: When You Feel Like a Nut!

Nuts are high on every allergen list. One reason might be the fact that nuts are rarely properly prepared for our bodies to digest easily. Nuts have a built-in protective element, called phytates, designed to keep them intact as they pass through our digestive system. In so doing, they actually pull minerals out of the body to prevent our metabolic enzymes from doing their job.[28] This is called anti-nutrients.

The method of soaking beans, seeds, and nuts helps break down this protective (and mildly toxic) casing. Soaked beans, seeds, and nuts become more easily digested, and, subsequently, all the nutrients can be used by the body. Soaking results in a much better flavor, too.

---

28   L. Hallberg, "Wheat Fiber, Phytates and Iron Absorption," supplement, *Scandinavian Journal of Gastroenterology* 129 (1987): 73–79.

Preparation Changes Everything

You'll find that the simple process of soaking nuts and beans also reduces the embarrassing and funny little melodies that sometimes result from eating them. Ahem!

Obviously, those of you dealing with nut allergies shouldn't have them; but you can certainly consider preparing beans and seeds properly.

Soaking with Salt

Throw beans, nuts, or seeds in a pan and add 1 tablespoon of salt, apple cider vinegar, baking soda, or lemon juice. Fill the pan with tepid filtered water and cover.

Let the beans, nuts, or seeds soak overnight or during the day (7 hours is ideal). Strain and rinse.

Keep it simple, and do this when you can. Sometimes we snack on nuts when we're out and about, and they haven't been properly prepared. No stress; it's all about balance!

For nuts: Preheat the oven to 170°F (or lower if your oven allows it). Spread the nuts onto a baking sheet and let them sit in the oven for several hours until crispy. The taste is so much better.

For gluten-free grains (e.g., oats): Soak for as long as you can (preferably overnight) in equal amounts of filtered water and lemon juice or coconut yogurt. Simply add to the recipe, no rinsing required.

For beans: Let these soak longer, around 12 hours if possible.

Rinse the beans and put them back into the pot, then add filtered water and seasonings.

Bring the beans to a boil then lower the heat and simmer for 2 hours. (This craziness is why the slow cooker is so valuable!)

Nut Milk

Yields 1 quart

Delicious nut milk without the carrageenan found in store-bought varieties.

- 1 cup raw almonds or hazelnuts, soaked
- 3 cups warm filtered water
- 1 tablespoon raw honey
- 1 teaspoon vanilla extract (optional)
- Pinch colored salt

Blend the raw almonds or hazelnuts, filtered water, raw honey, vanilla (if using), and salt in a high-speed blender.

Strain the milk over a tall bowl either through cheesecloth or a towel over a metal strainer. Save the nut pulp for Nut Balls *(page 115)*.

Chill the milk in the refrigerator or drink warm.

OMG Ajonjoli Milk

Yields 1 gallon

This is a family favorite, full of vitamins and minerals, learned in Puerto Rico but replaced sugar with honey!

- 1 pound sesame seeds (ajonjoli)
- 1 gallon filtered water, divided
- 1 cup ice cubes
- 1 tablespoon vanilla extract
- ½ cup raw honey

Put the sesame seeds into a 2-quart pot over medium-low heat and slowly toast them until they are golden brown. The seeds will begin to pop!

Transfer the toasted seeds to a high-speed blender with roughly 3 cups of the filtered water, ice, vanilla, and raw honey. Mix on high speed for a minute, until the milk is a delicious beige color. Strain the milk through a metal sieve into a container and put this pulp back into the blender. Add another 3 cups of the water and repeat until the gallon of water is all blended.

After all the milk has been blended, shake or stir the container to evenly distribute the ingredients.

Nut Balls

Yields 4 to 6 servings

These balls are a great alternative to sugar-laden candy bars!

- 🍴 ½ cup sesame seeds
- 🍴 1 cup gluten-free oats, preferably soaked in ¼ cup Homemade GFCF Coconut Yogurt *(page 35)*
- 🍴 1 cup shredded coconut
- 🍴 1 cup nut butter or nut pulp
- 🍴 ½ cup ground flaxseed or whole chia seeds
- 🍴 ½ cup raw honey
- 🍴 1 teaspoon vanilla extract

Place the sesame seeds in a shallow dish.

Place the oats, coconut, nut butter or pulp, flaxseed or chia seeds, raw honey, and vanilla in a large bowl and stir with a fork until thoroughly mixed. Scoop out 1 teaspoon and roll into a ball. Roll the ball in the sesame seeds to cover it. Repeat the process with the remaining oat-nut mixture. Put the balls in the refrigerator for 1 hour to harden up a bit.

Date Balls

Yields 4 to 6 servings

These balls are quick and easy—perfect for when you have unexpected company and need dessert fast.

- ¶ 1 cup Medjool dates and or raisins
- ¶ ¼ cup almonds
- ¶ ¼ cup walnuts
- ¶ ½ cup sesame seeds, for rolling

Remove any pits from the dates. Place the dates, almonds, and walnuts in the blender or food processor. Blend into a paste.

Take 1 tablespoon of the nut paste and roll it into a ball. Repeat this process with the remaining nut paste.

Pour the sesame seeds into a small bowl and roll the Nut Balls in them until they are covered with seeds.

Lentil Soup

Yields 4 to 6 servings

Mmmm . . .

- 2 (15-ounce) cans lentils or 3 cups soaked and rinsed lentils
- 3 cups chicken or beef stock
- 2 cups filtered water
- 2 carrots, cut into ¼-inch thick slices
- 1 large potato, chopped into ½-inch pieces
- 1 medium onion, chopped into ½-inch pieces
- 2 garlic cloves, minced
- 1 (½-inch) ginger knob, grated
- ½ teaspoon dried thyme
- ½ teaspoon curry powder
- ½ teaspoon dried oregano
- ½ teaspoon ground cumin
- ¼ teaspoon ground cinnamon
- ¼ teaspoon red pepper flakes
- 1 (3-inch) lemongrass stem or 2 teaspoons lemongrass paste
- ½ pound sliced gluten-free uncured chicken or turkey sausage (optional)
- Salt, to taste

After soaking the lentils as described in the beginning of this chapter (if not using canned lentils), put the lentils, chicken or beef stock, and filtered water in a large stock pot. Add the carrots, potato, onion, garlic, ginger, thyme, curry powder, oregano, cumin, cinnamon, red pepper flakes, lemongrass, sausage (if using), and salt. Cover, bring to a boil, reduce, and simmer on medium-low heat for 2 hours, or until the lentils are done.

Chapter 13: Fat Is Phat

Every cell of every tissue that makes up every organ in your body is comprised of fat! And the good fats, properly prepared, are brain food, as well as a support to our entire body. Fats are cofactors to minerals, which means that without fats, our bodies cannot maintain a healthy mineral balance.[29]

For example, Dr. Mary Enig, a noted nutritional biochemist and expert on fats, along with Sally Fallon of the Weston A. Price Foundation, researched and observed that moms who ate trans-fatty acids (a.k.a. bad fats) while pregnant became obese due to lack of satiation, and that many of their babies had vision problems.[30] Dr. Enig also published findings that the consumption of vegetable oils seems to increase the risks of cancer, while the consumption of animal fats seemed to protect against cancer.[31]

---

29   M. G. Enig, R. J. Munn, and M. Keeney, "Dietary Fat and Cancer Trends—A Critique," *Federation Proceedings* 37, no. 9 (July 1978): 2215–2220.

30   Mary Enig and Sally Fallon, *Eat Fat, Lose Fat: The Healthy Alternative to Trans Fats*.

31   See note 11.

Another major benefit of eating good fats in moderation is feeling satiated. That's right! High quality, good-tasting, nutrient-dense fats are satisfying, and a little goes a long way. So eating real, unmodified saturated fats in balance will help you stay strong and even lose extra body weight![32]

Beneficial Fats That Are Casein-Free

Below is a list of beneficial fats, many of which are utilized in this book:

- Bacon grease
- Coconut oil
- ★Ghee (see index)
- Olive oil
- Red palm oil
- Schmaltz (chicken fat)
- Tallow (beef fat)

---

32   See note 25.

Mom to Mom

Our family is mostly blood type O. There are predispositions and foods that are more beneficial for each type. Cooking with fats is critical for food to taste good. And the choices are mostly in the animal world. We noticed a difference quickly when we found the Blood Type Diet, because I had *leaned* more vegetarian at the time. Getting optimal health is the real goal and we noticed more energy when we began utilizing the fats of our meat.

Animal fats have huge benefits for us, and it works easily in a real-food, GFCF diet, but it certainly was an adjustment. The most noticeable difference is that it doesn't take much in a pan (a teaspoon to a tablespoon at the most).

Realistically, we practice the 80/20 rule loosely. Especially with foster and adopted kids of different blood types.

—Mandy

Bacon Fat

Yields about ½ cup bacon fat

Try beef bacon with this recipe!

🍴 1 (16-ounce) package bacon

Preheat the oven to 325°F.

Place the bacon strips very close together on a baking sheet and bake them for 30 to 40 minutes.

Remove the bacon quickly and eat it or use it in your favorite recipe!

While the fat is still warm, pour it into a mason jar (as shown above) and store for later. Bacon grease is really tasty with fried eggs.

Avocado À La Mode

Yields 6 servings

This is a super-fast recipe that boosts the brain power!

🍴 3 avocados, pitted and peeled

🍴 Salad Dressing of choice for drizzling

🍴 Salt and pepper, to taste

Put each avocado half on a plate. Drizzle each half with the Salad Dressing. Season with salt and pepper to taste and enjoy.

Olive Oil Salad Dressing

Yields about 12 ounces

This easy-to-make salad dressing contains good polyunsaturated fats, making your salad even more healthful!

- 1/3 cup apple cider vinegar or balsamic vinegar
- 1 tablespoon prepared mustard
- 1 tablespoon pumpkin or flaxseed oil (optional)
- ¾ to 1 cup olive oil, or to taste
- ½ teaspoon paprika
- ½ teaspoon dried minced garlic or garlic powder
- ½ teaspoon dried thyme
- ¼ teaspoon cayenne pepper
- ½ teaspoon salt

Put the vinegar, mustard, pumpkin or flaxseed oil, olive oil, paprika, dried minced garlic or garlic powder, thyme, cayenne pepper, and salt in a quart jar. Put the lid on the jar and shake vigorously for a delicious salad dressing that is budget-friendly, healthful, and resourceful.

Dark Cacao Coconut Cups

Yields 2 ice cube molds or about 12 extra-small cup liners

A delicious treat that delivers good fat and joy!

- 1 cup coconut oil
- ¼ cup raw cacao powder or 1 tablespoon cacao liquor
- ¼ cup raw honey
- ¼ cup cocoa butter
- 1 teaspoon vanilla extract

Mix together the coconut oil, cacao powder or cacao liquor, raw honey, cocoa butter, and vanilla in a small saucepan over low heat and stir until all the ingredients are melted.

Pour or spoon the melted mixture into ice cube molds or extra-small cupcake liners that rest on a plate. Refrigerate the Dark Cacao Coconut Cups to harden for 1 hour.

Bacon Beet and Plantain Chips

Yields about 10 ounces

"Beet" the plain stuff! Vitamins, minerals, and good fats!

- 3 to 4 pieces bacon (I recommend beef bacon)
- 1 large green plantain
- 3 medium beets
- 1 teaspoon salt
- 2 cups filtered water
- Garlic salt, to taste

Preheat the oven to 380°F.

Place 2 strips of bacon on a baking sheet.

Bake the bacon for 20 minutes, then remove from the oven. Stir and spread the beef bacon fat around the pan.

Wash the beets well and cut them into ½-inch thick slices. Cut the ends off the green plantain and slice lengthwise. Carefully break off the peel, then cut the plantain into about ¼-inch thick slices. (You can use a cheese grater to slice the plantain and beets, if desired.) Rinse the plantains in the salt and filtered water, then pat dry. When the bacon is cooked, remove the pan from the oven and place the sliced beets and plantains on the baking sheet as close together as possible. Sprinkle with the garlic salt to taste.

Bake the chips another 30 minutes or until crispy. (I take out the plantain chips and let the beets cook 10 minutes more.) Toss them together in a bowl and enjoy.

Schmaltz Beet and Plantain Chips

Yields about 10 ounces

For those of you who prefer chicken!

- 4 chicken wings or 3 tablespoons chicken fat from stock
- 3 medium beets
- 1 large green plantain
- 1 teaspoon salt
- 2 cups filtered water
- Garlic salt, to taste

Preheat the oven to 380°F.

Place the chicken wings or chicken fat on a baking sheet and cook the wings for 20 minutes or until the fat is melted. Remove the baking sheet from the oven.

Wash the beets well and cut them into ½-inch thick slices. Cut the ends off the green plantain and slice lengthwise. Carefully break off the peel, then cut the plantain into about ¼-inch thick slices. (You can use a cheese grater to slice the plantain and beets, if desired.) Rinse the plantains in the salt and filtered water, then pat dry. When the bacon is cooked, remove the pan from the oven and place the sliced beets and plantains on the baking sheet as close together as possible. Sprinkle with the garlic salt to taste.

Bake the chips another 30 minutes or until crispy. (I take out the plantain chips and let the beets cook 10 minutes more.) Toss them together in a bowl and enjoy.

Coconut and Red Palm Beet and Plantain Chips

Yields about 10 ounces

Because you can never have too many chips. You can find plantains fried in red palm oil at convenience stores, and it's a great travel option.

- 1 large green plantain
- 3 medium beets
- 1 teaspoon salt, plus more to taste
- 2 cups filtered water
- 2 tablespoons coconut oil
- 2 tablespoons red palm oil

Preheat the oven to 380°F.

Wash the beets well and cut them into ½-inch thick slices. Cut the ends off the green plantain and slice lengthwise. Carefully break off the peel, then cut the plantain into about ¼-inch thick slices. (You can use a cheese grater to slice the plantain and beets, if desired.) Rinse the plantains in the salt and filtered water, then pat dry. Put the coconut and red palm oil on the baking sheet and heat in oven for a few minutes and stir. Remove the pan from the oven and place the sliced beets and plantains on the baking sheet as close together as possible. Sprinkle with salt to taste.

Bake the chips for 30 minutes or until crispy. (I take out the plantain chips and let the beets cook 10 minutes more.) Toss them together in a bowl and enjoy.

Fat Flower Eggs

Yields 4 to 6 servings

Eggs are a perfect flower of health: protein surrounding a yellow, fatty center.

- Ghee, coconut oil, or red palm oil, for frying
- 1 medium red bell pepper, sliced ½-inch thick
- 1 medium orange bell pepper, sliced ½-inch thick
- 1 medium yellow bell pepper, sliced ½-inch thick
- 1 medium green bell pepper, sliced ½-inch thick
- 6 eggs
- 1 teaspoon paprika
- 1 teaspoon Papaya Pepper *(page 77)*

Heat a few tablespoons of the ghee, coconut oil, or red palm oil in a large skillet over medium heat. Place the sliced peppers in the skillet. Crack the eggs into the inside of the sliced peppers. Chop the remaining peppers into ½-inch pieces and place in the pan. Sprinkle with the paprika and Papaya Pepper.

Cover the skillet with a lid to allow the top of the egg to cook faster. Cook for about 3 minutes.

Bon appétit!

Chapter 14: Flowery Flora—Fermented Foods

Ohne effective way to restore good health is to increase your intestinal flora for dynamic digestion and brain health:

"Properly controlled fermentation may amplify the specific nutrient and phytochemical content of foods, the ultimate value of which may be associated with mental health; furthermore, the microbes (for example, Lactobacillus and Bifidobacteria species) associated with fermented foods may also influence health via direct and indirect pathways."[33]

Getting Started with Fermented Foods

Ideally, a little fermented food should accompany every cooked meal. Homemade GFCF Yogurt *(page 35)* can be a great addition. Even when dining out, you can find fermented foods—most Indian and Mediterranean restaurants serve yogurt with a meal, and it is simply delicious. There are many options that support the gut: sauerkraut, pickles, and homemade soda (recipes follow).

If you are new to fermented foods, introduce them slowly, about a tablespoon at a time. It takes time to repopulate your gut with friendly new microbes!

---

33   See note 3.

Basic Ginger Bug

Yields about 1 quart

This is a perfect GFCF fermenting base.

- 3 tablespoons grated fresh ginger
- 3 tablespoons cane sugar to feed the ferment (like a good beer)
- 5 tablespoons filtered water

Add the ginger, cane sugar, and filtered water to a clean quart-size mason jar. Stir to combine the ingredients, place the lid on the jar, and put the jar on the kitchen counter.

Continue adding to this same jar, repeating the above process with fresh ingredients added every day for 5 to 6 days. Swirl the ingredients to combine the new ingredients with the older ingredients, put the lid on the jar loosely, and leave the jar on the counter.

On the sixth or seventh day, you will have accumulated about a quart of Basic Ginger Bug. Swirl the ingredients to combine, but this time press and strain out all the liquid through a fine strainer and into a bowl. Pour this amazing ginger bug juice into a new quart jar and refrigerator.

Add to your drinks for a refreshing twist or add to make ferments.

Fizztacular Apple Soda Pop

Yields 1 gallon

Can you see the delicious bubbly probiotics?

- 1/3 cup raw honey or evaporated cane sugar
- 1/3 cup live Basic Ginger Bug
- 1 gallon apple juice in a demijohn or glass container, minus 8 ounces (for space)

Add the raw honey or cane sugar and Basic Ginger Bug to the apple juice. Put the lid back on the apple juice and shake to combine the ingredients. Place the juice in a warm spot (like the kitchen counter) for 3 to 5 days.

Open the lid daily to test the fizz (this is very important). When it makes a "pshhh" sound like when you open a soda can, it is done. You can taste test during the process by pouring a bit of juice into a cup until the desired fizz is achieved.

When a desired balance of sweetness and fizziness is obtained, simply tighten the lid and place in the refrigerator to chill.

Note: If a bit of white foam is on top, it's usually beneficial yeast from brewing. Just pour or scoop it out with a spoon. If you forget it and leave out a few days too long, it's cider and not for the kids anymore, only adults. If you forget for a week, be careful opening—it will erupt upon opening and can be used as apple cider vinegar!

"Give Me a Beet" Coleslaw Sauerkraut

Yields 2 quarts

This dish offers gallbladder support and digestive support.

- 1 (1-gallon) bag prepared coleslaw mix (undressed) or 1 large head cabbage, shredded
- 2 large beets, shredded
- 2 tablespoons salt
- 1/3 cup live-enzyme juice (such as Basic Ginger Bug or sauerkraut juice from purchased kraut)
- Filtered water, as needed

Put the coleslaw mix or shredded cabbage, beets, salt, and live-enzyme juice in a large bowl. Let this sit for up to 1 hour.

Divide the cabbage mixture between 2 quart-size mason jars and mash it down with your fist or the end of a wooden spoon.

Gently pour the filtered water on top to cover the veggies, leaving 1 inch of air space between the lid and the sauerkraut. Cover the jars, but not too tightly. Place the sauerkraut jars in a corner for 2 to 3 days.

You will see bubbles and possible spillage as the sauerkraut ferments, so it is a good idea to put the jar on top of a paper plate.

After 3 days, put the jars in the refrigerator.

Note: You can also buy sauerkraut, but it is cheap, simple, and very beneficial to make.

Super Simple Two-Day Pickles

Yields 1 quart

Who doesn't love pickles?

- 4 to 6 small unwaxed cucumbers
- 2 garlic cloves, mashed
- 1 tablespoon salt
- ½ teaspoon mustard seeds
- ½ teaspoon coriander seeds
- ½ teaspoon whole peppercorns
- ½ teaspoon cardamom seeds
- 1 to 2 sprigs fresh dill
- 2 large grape leaves from an 8-ounce jar of grape leaves
- Filtered water, as needed

Fill a quart-size mason jar with the cucumbers but leave 2 inches of space at the top of the jar. Add the garlic, salt, mustard seeds, coriander seeds, peppercorns, cardamom seeds, dill, and grape leaves. Fill the jar with filtered water, but leave 1 inch of air space at the top. Screw the lid on and leave the jar on the counter for 1 to 2 days. Then, place the jar in the refrigerator, and enjoy the pickles while they last!

Tip: The salt keeps the bad bacteria at bay while the good enzymes of the cucumber begin to break down, which is what "ferments" and creates pickles.

Probiotic Salad Dressing

Yields 1 ½ cups

When buying organic fermented food, it's expensive. This is a resourceful way to stretch your money and is also a conscious form of recycling.

- 1/3 cup leftover juices of fermented artichokes, pickles, or sauerkraut
- 1 tablespoon prepared mustard
- 1 tablespoon pumpkin or flaxseed oil (optional)
- ¾ to 1 cup olive oil, or to taste
- Salt, to taste
- ½ teaspoon dried oregano
- ½ teaspoon dried thyme
- ½ teaspoon garlic powder
- ½ teaspoon paprika

In a Pint or Quart jar, add the leftover fermented juices, mustard, pumpkin or flaxseed oil (if using), olive oil, salt, oregano, thyme, garlic powder, and paprika. Cover tightly.

Shake vigorously for a delicious salad dressing that is budget-friendly, healthful, and resourceful!

Chapter 15: Breaking Bread

Reducing Our Bread Consumption

The goal here, of course, is to reduce or eliminate the intake of gluten products and processed breads. This is no easy feat! Bread seems to be everywhere, and, well, sometimes it feels like sabotage.

Cake is bread.

Pasta is bread.

Appetizers are usually breaded.

Soups are generally filled with bready pastas and glutens.

Even prepared salads often contain gluten.

Sheesh!

True, there are gluten-free bakeries that make expensive cakes, and there are gluten-free cake mixes and gluten-free flours that you can find at the grocery store. It's all very processed and yummy in small doses for special occasions, but it's not great to eat that stuff on a regular basis for those of us recovering our health. Still, when something out of the ordinary is called for, you should certainly go for it! Order that cake or buy gluten-free flour and use the recipe on the back.

For the average day, though, when you get that bread craving, here are some super satisfying recipes that you're sure to enjoy.

Banana Blender Pancakes

Yields 4 to 6 servings

Who says GFCF eliminates pancakes?

- 2 large bananas
- 4 eggs
- Pinch salt
- Coconut oil, for frying

Blend the bananas, eggs, and salt in a blender.

Heat 2 tablespoons coconut oil in a medium skillet over medium heat.

Pour the batter into the skillet in ½-cup portions. Fry each pancake until browned, then flip and cook until browned on the other side.

Pumpkin Blender Pancakes

Yields 4 to 6 servings

These pancakes make such a yummy breakfast.

- 2 cups almond or coconut milk, divided
- 2 cups soaked oats
- 1 teaspoon apple cider vinegar
- 1 teaspoon baking soda
- ½ cup pumpkin puree
- 2 teaspoons ground cinnamon
- Pinch salt
- 1 teaspoon vanilla extract
- ½ teaspoon ground ginger
- Coconut oil, for frying
- Raw honey, for serving
- Maple syrup, for serving
- Homemade GFCF Yogurt for serving *(page 35)*

Combine 1 cup of the almond or coconut milk, oats, apple cider vinegar, and baking soda in a bowl. Cover the bowl and allow the ingredients to soak for a few hours or overnight on the kitchen counter.

Transfer the soaked ingredients to a blender along with the remaining 1 cup almond or coconut milk, pumpkin puree, cinnamon, salt, vanilla, and ground ginger. Blend well.

Heat a medium skillet over medium heat and add 1 to 2 tablespoons coconut oil per batch of pancakes. Pour about ½ cup batter from the blender into the skillet. Fry the pancake until golden and flip to fry the other side until golden.

Drizzle with the raw honey, maple syrup, or Homemade GFCF Yogurt.

Carob Zucchini Brownies

Yields 4 to 6 servings

These brownies are great for celebrations, bake sales, or any time you need a milk-free "chocolate fix."

- 1 large zucchini, cut into 1-inch round pieces
- 10 large Medjool dates
- ½ cup coconut flour
- ½ cup carob powder
- 5 eggs
- ½ cup ghee or coconut oil
- 1 teaspoon vanilla extract
- ½ teaspoon baking soda
- ½ teaspoon baking powder
- ½ teaspoon colored salt
- ½ cup carob chips

Preheat the oven to 350°F.

Put the zucchini, dates, coconut flour, carob powder, eggs, ghee or coconut oil, vanilla, baking soda, baking powder, and salt in a blender or food processor and blend until smooth. Fold in the carob chips.

Grease an 8-inch round or 9 x 5-inch loaf pan with additional coconut oil or line it with parchment paper. Pour the batter into the prepared pan.

Bake the brownies for 1 hour or until done. Insert a clean knife and if only melted carob chips are on the knife and no batter, the brownies are done.

Slow Cooker Breakfast Oat Porridge

Yields 6 to 8 servings

Prepare this porridge the day before and awake to an amazing breakfast.

- 2 cups soaked gluten-free steel-cut or whole oats
- 1 cup Homemade Coconut Yogurt *(page 35)*
- 2 cups coconut milk
- ½ cup raisins or 5 large Medjool dates, coarsely chopped
- 2 cups filtered water
- ½ teaspoon colored salt

Put the oats and homemade coconut yogurt in the slow cooker to soak for 7 hours (*do not* turn the slow cooker on while the oats are soaking). After soaking the oats, add the coconut milk, raisins or dates, filtered water, and salt. Cook the porridge on low overnight or for 7 hours. Add more water for a thinner consistency.

Green Plantain Waffles Extraordinaire

Yields 4 to 6 servings

Keeping the food real!

- 3 large green plantains
- 5 eggs
- 2 teaspoons ground cinnamon
- Maple syrup, for serving
- Raw honey, for serving

Place the plantains, eggs, and cinnamon in a blender. Blend until smooth.

Oil a waffle maker with coconut oil or other fat and pour in 1/3 cup of the batter when the waffle maker is warm.

When the waffle maker's indicator light shows "ready," let the waffle cook 3 more minutes to firm. Transfer the waffles to a plate and drizzle them with maple syrup or raw honey for fluffy, delicious waffles.

Waffle Burger Sliders

Yields 4 to 6 servings

A great whole-food, gluten-free bun idea that doesn't crumble. And it's simple enough to make at home! This recipe was discovered during a trip to Puerto Rico. There were a lot of plantains available behind our rental home, and this concoction has been our family's secret recipe ever since!

- 3 large green plantains
- 5 eggs
- 2 garlic cloves, minced, or 2 teaspoons garlic powder
- 2 teaspoons salt

Place the plantains, eggs, garlic or garlic powder, and salt in a blender. Blend until smooth.

Oil a waffle maker with coconut oil or other fat and pour in 1/3 to ½ cup of the batter when the waffle maker is warm.

When the waffle maker's indicator light shows "ready," let the bun cook 2 to 3 more minutes. Transfer the bun to a plate. Cut along the waffle seams and make a delicious burger.

Banana-Coconut French Toast

Yields 6 servings

No need to give up the classics when you're living GFCF.

Bread

- 6 eggs
- ½ cup raw honey or 1 cup evaporated cane sugar
- 2 large bananas, mashed
- ¾ cup potato starch

Preheat the oven to 350°F.

Blend the eggs, raw honey or cane sugar, bananas, and potato starch in a blender. Pour the batter into a greased 8-inch pan and bake for about 15 to 25 minutes. Cut the bread into squares. (It can be frozen for later use at this point.)

Batter

- 3 eggs
- 1 (15-ounce) can full-fat coconut milk
- 2 teaspoons ground cinnamon
- 3 to 4 tablespoons coconut oil or ghee, for frying

Mix the eggs, coconut milk, and cinnamon together in a medium mixing bowl. Submerge each of the bread squares in the batter.

Heat the coconut oil or ghee in a large skillet over medium-high heat and fry the coated bread for approximately 5 minutes on each side, until golden and crispy.

Slow Cooker Banana Bread

Yields 6 to 8 servings

This recipe makes a beautiful, moist, cake-like banana bread.

- 1 cup coconut flour
- 1 cup tapioca flour
- 5 large, ripe bananas
- 5 eggs
- 2 teaspoons vanilla extract
- 1 cup coconut oil or ghee
- 3 tablespoons fresh or bottled lemon juice
- 1 teaspoon baking soda
- Pinch salt
- 3 tablespoons sunchoke flour (optional)
- 2/3 cup coconut sugar or cane sugar

Turn the slow cooker on to the low setting. Grease the slow cooker with coconut oil.

Place the coconut flour, tapioca flour, bananas, eggs, vanilla, coconut oil or ghee, lemon juice, baking soda, salt, sunchoke flour (if using), and sugar in a blender and blend until smooth.

Pour the batter into the slow cooker and cook for about 3 to 4 hours.

Moonshine Bread

Yields 1 loaf

There is a nutritional discussion going on regarding consumption of too much starch, which can result in difficulty digesting complex sugars for a recovering gut. Since we ferment cabbage and juice to make it more beneficial, why couldn't we ferment plantains? This will reduce the sugar load in them, and it surprisingly doesn't taste sour. It allows the "bread" to rise very fluffy. **Note:** Plan ahead with this recipe, as it takes two days to prepare.

- 2 large or 3 small green plantains
- 1 tablespoon colored salt
- Filtered water, as needed
- 4 eggs
- 1 tablespoon ground cinnamon (optional)

Cut the ends off of the plantains and cut them lengthwise in order to peel out the meat. Place the plantains in a quart-size mason jar. Add the salt and fill half of the mason jar with filtered water.

On top of the submerged plantains, in the center, carefully place a shot glass right-side up to hold air inside. (This will help hold down the plantains.)

Carefully fill the rest of the jar with filtered water, but keep the shot glass empty. Quickly press the lid on top to hold the shot glass upright.

Place the jar of plantains on your kitchen counter for 24 hours.

Once ready, preheat the oven to 360°F.

Strain and rinse the plantains. (It will smell a little like moonshine!)

Transfer the fermented plantains to a blender. Add the eggs and cinnamon. Blend until smooth.

Line a 9 x 5-inch loaf pan or a 9 x 9-inch pan with parchment paper.

Pour the batter into the pan and bake for 50 minutes, or until golden brown.

We love to spread coconut oil on this bread and toast it!

Chapter 16: Party Time!

Photo by Picture People, Mandy's Children

We Have to Party!

Something in human nature needs to celebrate. Unfortunately, it seems that parties and junk food go hand in hand. Snacks and candy are by far the toughest arenas with food. Celebrations need to be fun . . . and that includes fun food!

The challenge is minimizing sugar, as it feeds the abnormal flora in our guts. Our family calls it the "sugar robber." Sugar will further exacerbate a compromised gut, as you already know.

But what do we do? Because we *have* to party! Let's just say a replacement is needed—and a tasty one. One great way is to replace white, refined sugar intake with a more nutrient-dense option. Raw honey, maple syrup, coconut sugar, and evaporated cane sugar still contain minerals and other nutrients. These sweeteners have not been bleached, either, so they are a more real-food option.

So, when it's party time, indulging moderately with these healthier options works great for our friends and family.

Mom to Mom

I remember when my four-year-old son was found under the table at 5 a.m. I had walked downstairs because there was a noise. Then I saw under the table a tub of ice cream and my little ASD child, with his head practically inside.

This went on for years; no matter where we hid the treats, he would find them! We would laugh in disbelief that he could consume such masses of sweets. Finally, we gave up hiding and just got rid of sweets and jumped on board the whole-food, real-food GFCF train. Our son's intense love of sugar, and his inability to resist, finally tipped the scales. It just didn't seem fair to have it around when he couldn't partake. Now, of course, we understand that he was feeding the wrong microbiome of the gut, which made his symptoms worse. But today, off sugar, he is vastly improved.

—Mandy

Raw Nut Brownies

Yields 6 to 8 servings

These brownies are so rich, a little goes a long way!

- 2 cups raw nuts (hazelnuts, cashews, almonds, or pecans), preferably soaked and crisped (see index)
- 1 large banana
- 1 teaspoon vanilla extract
- 1 tablespoon cacao or carob powder

Put the nuts, banana, vanilla, and cacao or carob powder in a blender or food processor. Pulse until the ingredients are combined and smooth but not turned into nut butter.

Spread the batter in a 9 x 9-inch brownie pan lined with parchment paper. Place the brownies in the refrigerator to firm up for at least 30 minutes.

Cut the brownies into squares and serve.

Pear Pie

Yields 7 "pies"

Yum.

- 7 medium to large firm pears
- ¼ cup walnuts or pecans, chopped
- 1 tablespoon ground cinnamon
- ½ cup soaked gluten-free rolled oats
- ½ cup Medjool dates, diced, or raisins
- 3 tablespoons coconut oil, melted, plus more for drizzling

Preheat the oven to 350°F.

Cut the tops off the pears. Using a knife or grapefruit spoon, dig out the core of each pear. Remove any seeds, then chop up the cores' fruit into ¼-inch pieces and put them in a medium mixing bowl. Add the chopped walnuts or pecans, cinnamon, oats, dates or raisins, and coconut oil. Mix gently to combine.

Use a spoon to gently place the pear mixture back into each pear. (Fill each one generously.)

Transfer the pears to a glass or stainless steel 9 x 9-inch baking dish and drizzle with additional coconut oil.

Bake for 45 minutes.

Rice Pudding

Yields 4 to 6 servings

Comfort food we learned in Costa Rica, with a coconut twist.

- 2 cups brown rice
- ½ cup coconut yogurt *(page 35)*
- ½ cup filtered water, plus more as needed
- Pinch colored salt
- 5 cups coconut milk
- 2 tablespoons ground cinnamon
- ½ cup coconut sugar, date sugar, or evaporated cane sugar
- ½ cup Medjool dates, diced, or raisins
- 3 tablespoons coconut oil
- Toppings: raisins, chia seeds, flax seeds, cinnamon

Put rice and yogurt in the slow cooker, add the filtered water, and stir well to soak for 4 to 7 hours.

After soaking the rice, yogurt, and water, add the salt, coconut milk, cinnamon, sugar, dates or raisins, and coconut oil and turn the slow cooker on low.

Let the pudding cook overnight or for 7 hours, until done. Add additional filtered water as needed until the desired thickness is reached.

Serve the Rice Pudding in bowls and watch it disappear with adults and kids alike!

Coconut Mint Patties

Yields 2 ice cube trays

Good fat improves your mood! Enjoy these as a snack or after-dinner treat.

- 1 cup coconut oil
- 14 drops food-grade peppermint oil
- 1 to 2 tablespoons raw honey or maple syrup
- 1 tablespoon raw cacao powder (optional)

Mix the coconut oil, peppermint oil, raw honey or maple syrup, and cacao (if using) together in a medium bowl and pour the mixture into an ice cube tray. Chill in the refrigerator or freezer until they are firm.

Lemon-Lavender Gummies

Yields 2 ice cube trays

These little gems are great for digestion, joint care, and aging gracefully.

- ¶ Juice of 2 lemons
- ¶ 2 cups filtered water
- ¶ 3 tablespoons plain grass-fed beef gelatin
- ¶ ¼ cup raw honey
- ¶ 1 drop food-grade lavender essential oil

Put the lemon juice and filtered water in a medium saucepan over medium heat. Add the gelatin and whisk well. Heat the gelatin mixture until it starts to bubble. Turn off the heat and let the gelatin cool for 15 minutes.

Stir in the raw honey and lavender essential oil.

Pour the gelatin into silicone ice cube trays or mini-cups on a plate, and place them in the refrigerator.

The gummies are ready when they are fully gelled (about 1 hour).

Vanilla Ice Cream (with variations)

Yields 4 to 6 servings

This much-loved treat offers beneficial fat for healthy cells, tissues, organs, and organelle systems.

Vanilla

- 2 (15-ounce) cans full-fat coconut milk
- 1/3 to ½ cup raw honey or maple syrup
- 2 tablespoons vanilla extract

Put the coconut milk, raw honey or maple syrup, and vanilla in a blender and blend until the ingredients are combined.

Turn on an ice cream maker and pour the coconut milk mixture into the cylinder. Follow the ice cream maker's instructions for the churning process.

For flavor variations, follow the instructions above and add the ingredients below to the coconut milk mixture. Have fun and be creative!

Tip: If you choose to add fruit, we recommend putting it in a serving bowl; it can get too hard in the ice cream machine.

Carob

- Add 2 tablespoons carob powder or 3 tablespoons gluten-free carob chips.

Pecan

- Add 1 cup chopped pecans.

Ginger

- Add 1 tablespoon ground ginger and 2 teaspoons grated fresh ginger.

Lemon

- Add the juice of 3 lemons or 3 tablespoons bottled lemon juice.

Lavender

- Add 2 drops food-grade lavender oil. Sprinkle with dried lavender flowers for garnish.

Banana Caterpillars

Yields 4

For the kid in us all! These are a great source of potassium, fat, and protein.

- 4 large bananas
- Almond butter or Homemade Coconut Butter with Cacao (recipe follows), as needed
- Dried cherries or blackberries, for feet
- Raisins or GFCF carob chips, for eyes
- Shredded coconut

Give every child a plate, banana, and butter knife.

Cut the banana into bite-size pieces. Spread the almond butter or Homemade Coconut Butter with Cacao on the sliced end of each banana piece and press into the next banana piece until all slices are smeared with nut butter and the caterpillar is stuck together.

Lay down the dried cherries or blackberries along the length of the caterpillar for feet.

Put the raisins or carob chips on one end of the caterpillar for eyes. Sprinkle some shredded coconut around the caterpillar for a "landscape."

Have fun, and enjoy!

Homemade Coconut Butter with Cacao or Carob

Yields 1 cup

If there is a nut allergy in your family, maybe this spread will work. *Coconuts are not considered a true nut, but check with your doctor to see if you or your loved one is allergic first!*

- 1 cup shredded coconut
- 1 tablespoon coconut oil
- 1 tablespoon cacao or carob powder
- 1 teaspoon maple syrup, to taste

In a blender, blend the shredded coconut, coconut oil, cacao or carob powder, and maple syrup on high for 30 seconds. Stir and repeat until the desired smoothness is achieved.

Creamy Carob Monkey Ice Cream

Yields 4 servings

What an amazing frozen treat!

- 2 large bananas, peeled, broken into 2-inch pieces, and frozen
- 1 tablespoon carob powder
- 1 tablespoon raw honey
- ½ cup ice cubes
- 2 tablespoons nut butter (optional)
- 1 egg (optional)

In a blender or food processor, blend the bananas, carob powder, raw honey, ice cubes, nut butter (if using), and eggs (if using) until smooth.

Serve immediately.

Sweet Potato Soufflé

Yields 6 to 8 servings

Don't let the name of this recipe intimidate you. This is the easy version!

- 2 cups baked sweet potato
- 3 eggs
- ¾ cup raw honey
- 1 tablespoon grated fresh ginger
- 2 teaspoons ground cinnamon
- ¼ teaspoon salt
- 1 drop food-grade clove oil (optional)
- 1 teaspoon fresh lemon zest
- ½ cup coconut cream
- 2 tablespoons brandy (optional, but recommended)

Place the sweet potato, eggs, raw honey, ginger, cinnamon, salt, clove oil (if using), lemon zest, coconut cream, and brandy (if using) in a blender. Blend until smooth.

Preheat the oven to 350°F. Grease a muffin pan or a 9 x 9-inch glass baking dish with coconut oil.

Pour the sweet potato mixture into the muffin wells or baking dish and bake for 35 to 45 minutes.

Chapter 17: Crazy Mama

Every good thing comes with controversy. But I come in peace. The following are some of the methods I and my family have used and that have steered us toward a new level of recovery. Hopefully, this list inspires you to research the many available holistic approaches to health.

Blood Type Diet – A guide to the best foods for your body type. Kind of like figuring out if your engine needs unleaded, diesel, or an electrical charge.

Colonics (Colon Hydrotherapy) – An enema on steroids! A professional manages a flush with several gallons used to cleanse deeper into the bowels. The Gentle Rolling Method is preferred.

Cleaning Supplies – Remember there are some very effective cleaning ingredients that are cheap and accessible. Lemon, vinegar, and baking soda are nontoxic options that will keep the environment safer too.

Dental Care – Finding a natural and holistic dentist is important when dealing with immune-compromised children. Dental visits will be handled carefully and without excessive drugs. A simple, nontoxic toothpaste can be made with coconut oil, baking soda, and colored salt.

Enemas and Supplants – These are helpful for reducing fevers, cleansing the body of parasites and improving general malaise. These age-old therapies get directly to the gut. Flushing the gut and implanting probiotics[34] is a home remedy practiced commonly until recent years. Some children can't take pills well, so this approach is useful.

Hyperbaric Oxygen – Studies have shown mixed reviews with recovering cancer patients, stroke victims, individuals with autism, individuals with ASD, and more. Varying degrees of pressure and air pass through the blood-brain barrier to increase neurological functions and much more. For more information, a great video is noted from Dr. Allan Spiegel.[35]

Infrared Sauna – This is a heat-without-humidity sauna that detoxes through the skin in a dry environment.

---

34   J. Kałużna-Czaplińska and S. Błaszczyk, "The Level of Arabinitol in Autistic Children After Probiotic Therapy," *Nutrition* 28, no. 2 (February 2012):124–126.

35   "Dr. Allan Spiegel Interview – Hyperbaric Oxygen – Behm Natural Dentistry," YouTube video, 16:19, posted by "Ray Behm," August 3, 2015, https://youtu.be/HHnPfdnaXyc.

Ionic Foot Bath – This is an osmotic system that balances your body's electrical charge. Highly charged ions flood the body with negative ions and attract the free radicals, which can cause tremendous harm.

Supplements – There are some really amazing organic, gluten-free food supplements that have a powerful effect on recovery.

Skin – This is the largest organ on our body and we often forget it. If we put great food into our bodies but slather chemical goop *on* them, we reverse our good efforts. Activated charcoal and clay are great tools for our skincare routines. Visit www.ewg.org/skindeep to learn more about skincare products and companies.

A Quick Favor

If you greatly benefit your health by reading and eating from this brawny cookbook, please take a few minutes and review the book on Amazon. It will help more than you could ever imagine. And hopefully, you will continue to be inspired to be the greatest and healthiest you! Power on!

Join Me in Fostering Health!

If you'd like to connect with me and learn more about how you can foster health in any generation, sign up at: **RealFoodRecovery.org**

About the Author

J. Whitehead is quoted as saying, "Children are the living message we send to a time we will not see."

At age twelve, Mandy wanted to adopt a child. Learning that there were over four hundred thousand children in foster care was unthinkable! That dream took time, through many amazing adventures, and with children filling up all the spaces. At Cal Poly, Mandy graduated with fancy degrees and cooking and nutritional credentials, but the important stuff was how many children's homes were turned into mad houses. How each child is empowered to be awesome because of a special gift they possess!

Mandy loves sharing the importance of the food we put in our bodies. If you want to be great, you have to eat great! If you want to be fun, you must eat fun! Having four children, Mandy has now fostered ten children and adopted only one! Her inspiration to step out into the big world and share her story was through a little two-year-old foster boy with cancer who called her Mommy. After regaining most of his health with great food, and despite chemo, Dak moved back with his biological dad. Surviving on Cheetos, Coke, and marshmallows, Dak passed away at four years old. Mandy held this little guy in her arms as he passed, and his last words inspire Mandy today. Life comes with some powerful lessons. Mandy intends to use her experience, knowledge, and inspiration to reach out and help every kid and family she can touch through www.RealFoodRecovery.org. Join her to blow the roof off hate, fear, anger, prejudice, and the bad food that is killing our children and the earth. Fight with her for love, peace, forgiveness, and good, clean food that nourishes us all!

Index